Holt Middle School Math

Consumer and Career Mathematics
Course 2

HOLT, RINEHART AND WINSTON

A Harcourt Education Company

Orlando • **Austin** • New York • San Diego • Toronto • London

ISBN 0-03-066229-X

4 5   082   05 04

CONTENTS

Holt Middle School Math   Course 2

CONTENTS, *CONTINUED*

Holt Middle School Math   Course 2

Name _____ Date _____ Class _____

Career Math
Data Toolbox

City Planner

What They Do
A city planner studies a city's growth patterns and works to make improvements that will meet the needs of the people and their communities now and in the years to come. They collect, analyze, and interpret complex technical data from a variety of sources in order to guide them in difficult decision making processes.

City planners also read and interpret laws, regulations, maps, site plans, and building plans. They summarize technical information on planning issues by creating various data displays and illustrations to help depict the current situation and to assess the future trends and needs of their city. Planners often work with architects, engineers, construction contractors and other professionals in order to solidify their ideas.

The Degree Required
A Bachelor's Degree in Urban Planning or a Master's Degree in structural engineering

Math Courses Needed
Algebra, geometry, Computer-Aided Design, business math and statistics

Other Courses Needed
Courses in economics, business and computers are recommended.

How They Use Math
A city planner uses math to plot demographics and to analyze the results. The planner may see a trend that a particular area is losing population, and may decide to boost the economy in that area. In order accurately to assess environmental issues concerning new urban development, as well as transportation needs of growing cities, city planners maintain databases and formulate data into meaningful reports. Graphs, tables, and charts displaying data are typically used in project planning sessions.

Holt Middle School Math   Course 2

Name _____ Date _____ Class _____

Career Math
Data Toolbox, continued

The city planner needs to decide how to **zone** 250 acres of
undeveloped land in the northeast part of town. She will zone the
land as either single-family residential housing or multifamily
retirement housing.

A subcommittee presented the city planner with the following data.
The planner will examine the trends in population growth for each
age group and base her zoning decision on housing need.

Town Population From 1984 to 2002

Age	1984	1986	1988	1990	1992	1994	1996	1998	2000	2002
18–50 years	1,375	1,435	1,500	1,570	1,600	1,545	1,510	1,450	1,422	1,375
over 50 years	1,035	1,150	1,295	1,410	1,595	1,655	1,715	1,775	1,830	1,900

Using the data, the city planner created the following double bar graph.

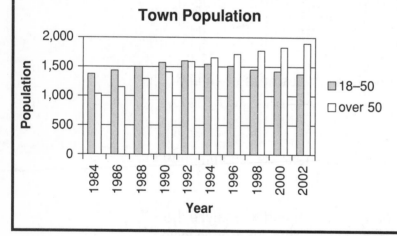

Use the information above for the following exercises.

1. Find the range of years that the
population for the 18 to 50 age group
increased.

2. Find the range of years that the
population for the over 50 age group
increased.

_____

_____

3. Given the current trend in population
estimate the population of the over
50 age group in 2004.

4. Based on the data, how would you
zone the property if you were the
City Planner?

_____

_____

Holt Middle School Math   Course 2

Name _____ Date _____ Class _____

Emily must report commission earnings of her sales department for the month of May to the regional sales office. Commission is a percent of the dollar value of sales over a specified period of time. In her report, she must provide the range, mean, median and mode of commissions paid for the month.

Commission Report

Employee	Jan	Feb	Mar	Apr	May
Janice	$650	$772	$595	$697	$750
Fred	$772	$489	$683	$805	$695
Jose	$598	$637	$783	$492	$767
Nicki	$650	$689	$675	$650	$695
Charlie	$805	$945	$595	$737	$595

Emily made the following calculations for her report.

Range $= \$767 - \$595 = \$172$ Subtract the smallest value from the greatest value.

Median $= \$695$ Arrange the values in numerical order and find the middle value.

Mode $= \$695$ Find the value that occurs most often.

Mean $= \dfrac{\$750 + \$695 + \$767 + \$695 + \$595}{5} = \$700.40$ Find the average.

Use the Commission Report table above for each exercise.

1. Find Jose's mean commission for the months January through May.

_____

2. What is the range of commission for Charlie over the past five months?

_____

3. How much less is the median commission for March than May?

_____

4. How much more is the mode for January and February than the mode for May?

_____

5. A bonus of $200 will go to any sales person who has a median commission greater than $695. Which employee(s) will get the bonus?

_____

6. Which employee(s) has a mean commission for the months shown greater than the mean commission for the month of May?

_____

LESSON 1-7 Consumer Math
Investment Stock

A line graph can be used to evaluate the performance of a company's **stock** over time. Individuals purchase stock as an **investment.** Stocks are sold by companies as a means of generating money. Typically, as performance increases, the return on investment increases. The line graph shows the performance of Tristate Restaurants over the past year. The investor can look at this graph to find trends in the stock performance and the relative health of the company.

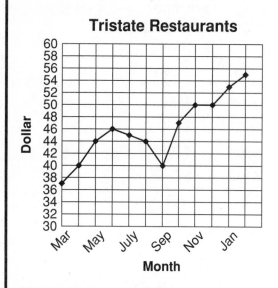

Tristate Restaurants

Use the line graph for each exercise.

1. During which month was there the biggest increase in stock price?

   _____

2. Overall, how much has the stock risen from last March to this February?

   _____

3. Using the same graph above, plot the points in the table below to make a double line graph.

Home Living Stock Prices

Mar	Apr	May	Jun	Jul	Aug	Sep	Oct	Nov	Dec	Jan	Feb
42	46	51	50	48	49	40	40	44	50	49	50

4. In the first six months, which company appears to have performed better?

   _____

5. During which month was there a sharp decrease in the value of the stock for both companies?

   _____

Career Math
Number Theory and Algebraic Reasoning

Astronomer

What They Do
Astronomers spend a great deal of their time working, teaching, or analyzing data as opposed to gazing at the stars. Astronomy is an observational science rather than an experimental science. Astronomers observe phenomena rather than perform experiments. They use high-powered telescopes, instruments and computers to collect data, and work with mathematicians and astrophysicists in making conclusions. Astronomers are often employed by colleges and universities as professors or in college-related observatories. Some work for the government or in private labs doing research and development projects; many work at planetariums.

The Degree Required
A Bachelor's Degree in astronomy or physics

Math Courses Needed
Algebra, geometry, finite mathematics, and calculus

Other Courses Needed
Courses in physics, chemistry, and computer science

How They Use Math
Mathematics is used extensively throughout the astronomical field. For example, astronomers collect and study data by tracking the energy given off by faint and distant stars and the cosmic movement of exotic planetary bodies like pulsars, quasars and nebulas. Then they try to predict how these phenomena interact. Astronomers use highly advanced technology and equipment and rely on their mathematical background to help them to formulate conclusions. They often use scientific notation to display their results.

Name _____ Date _____ Class _____

An astronomer works with numbers so large in size that it is cumbersome not only to write these numbers, but also very confusing when trying to work with them. Astronomers believe that there are 100 quintillion stars in the universe. Written in standard form this number would look like 100,000,000,000,000,000,000. It is easier for an astronomer to use a "shorthand" approach to displaying this number by writing it in scientific notation as 1×10^{20}.

It has been estimated that the distance to the sun is 93 million miles. Written in **standard form,** this number is written as 93,000,000 miles. Astronomers write this number using **scientific notation.** In scienic notation the number is written as two factors, one being a number greater than or equal to 1 and less than 10, and the other being a power of 10. The exponent is equal to the number of places the decimal point is moved.

$93,000,000. = 9.3 \times 10^7$

In scientific notation the number is written as 9.3×10^7.

Complete.

1. The distance from Mercury to the sun is 35,990,000 miles. Write this number in scientific notation.

2. The distance from Venus to the sun is 6.7239×10^7 miles. Write this number in standard form.

3. The distance from Mars to the sun is 1.4136×10^8 miles. Write this number in standard form.

4. The distance from Jupiter to the sun is 483,600,000 miles. Write this number in scientific notation.

5. The distance from Saturn to the sun is 887,220,000 miles. If you write the number in scientific notation, what is the exponent on the factor of 10?

6. The distance from Uranus to the sun is 1,783,700,000 miles. How many places do you have to move the decimal point to write the number in scientific notation?

Consumer Math

2-3 Total Pay

Raphael works for Hamburg Industries as an **hourly** employee. An hourly employee is paid for each hour spent working on the job. This is called **straight pay.** Typically, hourly employees are paid additional wages for any hours worked over a normal 40-hour work week. This is called **overtime pay.**

Raphael worked 63 hours last week. What was his total pay if his straight pay is $7.50 per hour and overtime pay is $11.25 per hour?

($7.50 × 40) + $11.25(63 − 40) Write an expression.

$300 + $11.25(23)   Perform operations in parentheses first.

$300 + $258.75   Multiply.

$558.75   Add.

Raphael's total pay for last week was $558.75.

Solve.

1. Kaitlin worked 56 hours this week. What was her total pay for the week if her straight pay is $8.00 per hour and overtime pay is $12.00 per hour?

2. Randolph earns $6.50 per hour straight pay and $9.75 per hour overtime pay. If he works 61 hours in a week, what will be his total pay?

3. Gary is paid $17.00 straight pay and $25.50 overtime pay. If he made $884.00 for the week, how many hours did he work?

4. Sandra made $656.00 last week. She earns $8.00 per hour straight pay and $12.00 per hour overtime pay. How many overtime hours did she work?

5. Nicholas is paid $9.50 per hour straight pay and $14.25 per hour overtime pay. He made $1,144.75 for the past two weeks he worked. How many overtime hours did he work over the last two weeks?

6. Muriel earned $1573.44 for the month of June. If she makes $7.25 per hour straight pay and $10.88 per hour overtime pay, how many overtime hours did she work for the month? (*Hint:* 4 weeks in a month)

Consumer Math

LESSON 2-7 *Piece-Work Wages*

Darian earns **piece-work wages** at Starlink Corporation. Employees who are paid piece-work wages are paid a specified amount of money for each article or unit produced. Each article or unit produced is called a **piece** and the dollar amount received for each piece is called the **piece rate.** Piece-work wages can be expressed as:

$W = p \times r$ Where W represents the wages, p represents the number of pieces produced, and r represents the piece-rate paid.

If Darian produced 235 circuit boards in a week and earns $411.25, find his piece-work rate.

$W = p \times r$ Write the formula.

$\$411.25 = 235 \times r$ Substitute known values in the equation.

$\dfrac{\$411.25}{235} = r$ Divide each side by 235 and solve for r.

$\$1.75 = r$

Darian makes a piece-work rate of $1.75.

Complete.

1. Diane is paid $1.35 for each unit produced. She earns $171.45 for the day. Write and solve an equation to find how many units she produced in a week.

2. Joshua earns 3 times as much as Tim for producing the same transistors. If each produces 176 units, write an expression to find Joshua's piece-work rate.

3. Mickey is paid $1.15 for each computer chip he produces. He worked five days last week. The first four days he produced 106 units, 97 units, 98 units and 102 units. His total wages for the week were $591.10. Write and solve an equation to find how many computer chips he made on the fifth day.

4. Kitrina is a seamstress in a garment factory. In an 8-hour workday she assembled 12 blouses and 2 skirts. She is paid $15.30 for each blouse she makes. She is paid $20.00 for each skirt she makes. Write and solve an equation to determine Kitrina's hourly rate.

CHAPTER 3 **Career Math**

Integers and Rational Numbers

Accountant

What They Do
Accountants take care of financial matters for individuals and for businesses. Accountants are knowledgeable of the latest tax laws. They prepare tax returns and financial statements on a timely basis. They are aware of the various forms of business ownership and advise their clients of the advantages and disadvantages of each. When performing some of these tasks, the accountant may work in conjunction with other professionals, such as attorneys and investment advisors.

The Degree Required
A Bachelor's Degree in accounting or in business management with an emphasis in accounting

Math Courses Needed
Algebra, calculus, and statistics

Other Courses Needed
Business management and communication are recommended. Most accountants increase their opportunities and pay level by taking the Certified Public Accountant exam, becoming a CPA. A CPA requires 40 hours of continuing education each year to maintain the license.

How They Use Math
Accountants use mathematics when preparing reports or taxes. For year-to-date comparisons and to make quick management decisions, financial reports are compiled monthly. The sales, gross profit, and net profit at the end of any given month, can be compared with prior years to get an idea of how the current year will finish.

Holt Middle School Math   Course 2

CHAPTER	**Career Math**
3	*Integers and Rational Numbers, continued*

Accountants often determine the **net income** or **net loss** for a corporation or sole proprietor for a certain period of time. This time period can be one month, 6 months, a year, or any other time period defined by the client. The formula used to determine net income (positive value) or loss (negative value) is:

Net Income or Loss = Revenue − Expenses

Revenue is the accounts represented by the sales of a product or service. **Expenses** are accounts that represent the cost of doing business.

Determine the net income or loss given the information in the table. The table is based on revenue and expenses for the past 6 months.

Hare Accessories

Revenue	$54,000
Rent	$724 per month
Salaries	$8,000
Supplies	$2,100

Net Income/Loss = Revenue − Expenses
$$= \$54,000 - [6(\$724) + \$8,000 + \$2,100]$$
$$= \$54,000 - [\$4,344 + \$8,000 + \$2,100]$$
$$= \$39,556$$

Since the result is positive, Hare Accessories shows a net income of $39,556 for the past 6 months.

Determine the net income or net loss.

1. Revenue = $16,000
Supplier Expense = $4,000
Salary Expense = $6,500

2. Sales Revenue = $1,350
Salaries Expense = $1,500
Advertising Expense = $350

3. In 3 months, Mime Inc. has recorded a service revenue of $5,800, rental expense of $1,250 per month, salary expense of $3,000 and a sales revenue of $5,200. How much money have they earned or lost in 3 months?

4. In 4 months, Data Inc. has recorded an insurance expense of $980 per month, service revenue of $4,800, and an advertising expense of $450 per month. How much money have they earned or lost in 4 months?

Holt Middle School Math **Course 2**

LESSON	**Consumer Math**
3-3	*Profit and Loss*

A **profit and loss statement** is a financial document that shows the annual overall profit or loss of a business. A profit and loss statement lists earnings for sales or services provided, the cost of goods or services provided, operating expenses such as wages paid, rent and advertising, and the total income or loss. Income items are positive numbers and expenses are negative numbers. By adding the income and expenses, the business owner can determine the overall profit or loss.

Last year a small business owner generated $230,000 in sales. He paid his employees $90,000 in wages, and spent $69,700 for rent, advertising and miscellaneous business expenses and supplies. Determine the overall profit or loss from the business.

$230,000 + (−$90,000) + (−$69,700)	Find the sum using negative numbers for expenses.
$230,000 − $90,000 − $69,700	Find the difference of the absolute values.
$70,300	The answer is positive.

The business made a $70,300 profit.

Solve.

1. Jerry made $4,000 mowing lawns over the summer. He spent $350 for a new lawn mower, $100 for advertising and $500 for gas. Did he make a profit or loss? How much was it?

2. Chris started an arcade business last year. The total earnings for the year were $140,700. The equipment and supplies to start the business cost $83,000; wages to employees were $56,160; rent was $7,500; and advertising cost $3,550. Did he make a profit or loss? How much was it?

3. Terry earned $31,250 for hanging wallpaper. He spent $625 for supplies and $1,275 for transportation costs. Did he make a profit or loss? How much was it?

Holt Middle School Math   Course 2

Name _____ Date _____ Class _____

Consumer Math
Average Daily Change

A business owner must keep track of the average daily change of money coming into and out of the business. To determine the average daily change, the bank account must be monitored to keep track of the deposits and withdrawals made each day. When a business owner has an accurate picture of money flow, he will be confident that money will be available to keep the operations of the business running smoothly.

The table below shows a businesses bank account deposits and withdrawals over a 7-day period. What is the average daily change of funds in the account?

Day	Sun	Mon	Tues	Wed	Thurs	Fri	Sat
Amount ($)	627	−375	652	558	−295	−598	726

$627 + (−375) + 652 + 558 + (−295) + (−598) + 726$ Find the sum of the changes in money.

$\frac{1295}{7} = 185$ Divide by 7 to find the average for the week.

The average daily change in the account is $185.

Use the table for each exercise.

Cash Flow for Animators Inc.

	Sun	Mon	Tues	Wed	Thurs	Fri	Sat
Week 1	$ 636	$−323	$ 422	$ 617	$−227	$−420	$ 730
Week 2	$ 123	$−416	$ 524	$ 619	$−322	$ 762	$−121
Week 3	$ 413	$−351	$−125	$ 752	$ 430	$−328	$ 630
Week 4	$ 224	$−275	$ 565	$−431	$ 692	$−123	$ 783

1. What was the average daily change in the account for week 2?

_____

2. What was the difference between the average daily change for week 1 and week 3?

_____

3. What was the average daily change for all 4 weeks (28 days)?

_____

Holt Middle School Math   Course 2

CHAPTER	**Career Math**
4	*Operations with Rational Numbers*

Nutritionists

What They Do
The main responsibility of a nutritionist is to promote good health by planning, creating, and implementing nutritional dietary programs. These programs are designed to prevent and treat illnesses by improving healthy eating habits and suggesting diet modifications, such as less salt for those with high blood pressure or reduced cholesterol intake for those with heart disease. Some nutritionists work for institutions such as hospitals and schools where they manage food service programs. They promote sound eating habits through education and often become involved in research that leads to significant improvements in the areas of health and nutrition. Major areas of practice include clinical, community, management, and consultant dietetics.

The Degree Required
A Bachelor's degree in dietetics, foods and nutrition, or food service systems management is required. Those interested in research, advanced clinical positions, or public health may need an advanced degree.

Math Courses Needed
Algebra, business mathematics, statistics and economics

Other Courses Needed
Courses in food science, nutrition, management, chemistry, biochemistry, microbiology and physiology are recommended.

How They Use Math
Nutritionists use math when structuring meal plans and diets for individuals or groups. They must accurately determine the amount of calories, fat, sodium and many other nutrients in the meal plans they create. They also use math when determining portion sizes and when converting menus and recipes from single serving to multiple servings. If involved in research, math is used to evaluate statistical data and to provide evidence that supports their particular research.

13 **Holt Middle School Math Course 2**

CHAPTER	# Career Math
4	## *Operations with Rational Numbers, continued*

Ms. Tabor is a dietitian for the local middle school. To achieve a vegetable requirement, she determines that potato salad should be served for lunch on Wednesdays. She has a recipe for potato salad that makes 10 servings. She needs to convert the recipe in order to make enough potato salad to serve 200 students. Using the recipe below, find the amount of potatoes needed to make 200 servings.

Potato Salad (Serves 10)

$3\frac{1}{6}$ pound potatoes $1\frac{3}{8}$ cups pickle relish

$1\frac{1}{4}$ pound onions $\frac{1}{4}$ tablespoon paprika

$\frac{5}{6}$ pound celery $\frac{1}{4}$ cup mustard

$\frac{2}{3}$ tablespoon pepper $\frac{1}{3}$ tablespoon salt

To convert the recipe to serve 200 students, first divide the number of servings needed by the number of servings of the recipe: $200 \div 10 = 20$. Then, multiply the amount of the ingredient, potatoes, by a factor of 20.

$3\frac{1}{6} \times 20$ Multiply pounds of potatoes in the recipe by 20.

$$3\frac{1}{6} \times 20 = \frac{19}{6} \times 20 = \frac{19}{\underset{3}{6}} \times \frac{\overset{10}{20}}{1} = \frac{190}{3} = 63\frac{1}{3}$$

In order to serve 200 students, $63\frac{1}{3}$ lbs of potatoes will be needed.

Solve.

1. Using the recipe for potato salad shown above, how many pounds of onions will you need to make 200 servings?

2. Using the recipe for potato salad shown above, how many cups of pickle relish will you need to make 50 servings?

3. One serving of the cafeteria's tomato soup contains 200 mg of sodium (salt). The school's dietitian suggests that a serving should only have $\frac{2}{3}$ of this amount. How many milligrams of sodium should the soup contain?

4. One serving of the cafeteria's chicken potpie contains 320 calories. The school's dietitian suggests that the football players eat $1\frac{2}{3}$ servings for lunch. How many calories are in $1\frac{2}{3}$ serving of potpie?

Name _____ Date _____ Class _____

Consumer Math
Budget Expenses

A **budget** is a spending and savings plan based on an estimate of income and expenses. While the main purpose of a budget is to help you live within your means, the budget process itself has many other benefits. It can help you save toward goals, identify spending patterns, and perhaps make changes in the way you spend your money. A budget should include fixed and variable expenses. **Fixed expenses** are costs such as car payments, and rent or mortgage payments that do not change each month. **Variable expenses** are costs such as food, utilities, phone bills, etc., that may change each month.

Category	Rent	Car	Phone	Food	Utilities	Total
Budgeted Amount	$500.00	$214.31				
Actual Expense Jan.	$500.00	$214.31	$42.55	$145.33	$176.33	
Actual Expense Feb.	$500.00	$214.31	$38.21	$119.56	$177.98	
Actual Expense Mar.	$500.00	$214.31	$39.87	$112.78	$181.24	

The spreadsheet above represents Maria Moeller's personal **budget.** How much should Maria budget for her utilities?

To determine the amount to budget for a variable expense, compute a multiple month average. The average amount of Maria's utilities can be found by adding the actual expenses for January, February and March, and dividing the result by the total number of months, 3.

$$\frac{\$176.33 + \$177.98 + \$181.24}{3} = \$178.52$$

Maria should budget $178.52 for her utilities.

Use the information above for each problem.

1. How much should Maria budget each month for food?

2. How much should Maria budget each month for phone expenses?

3. How much should Maria's total monthly budget be for all of her fixed and variable expenses?

4. Maria's monthly car payment is a fixed expense. How much will Maria have paid after one full year of payments?

Name _____ Date _____ Class _____

Consumer Math

LESSON 4-3 *Purchase Order Forms*

For record keeping purposes, many companies use **purchase order forms** when purchasing various quantities of items. A purchase order form shows the item number, a description, the quantity ordered, the unit price, the amount for each item, and the total amount to be purchased.

Purchase Order Form

Item	Description	Quantity	Unit Price	Amount
A3321	Ink Pens	12	$0.23	
A3556	Black Markers	4	$0.51	
C9987	Color Printer Cartridge	2	$21.33	
C7765	Computer Paper (Box)		$5.36	$21.44
D0012	Paper Clips (Box)	5		$4.15
			Total Purchase	

Roberto is an administrative assistant for the local electric company. One of his responsibilities is to order office supply items using a purchase order form, as shown above. What is the total amount Roberto should enter for the ink pens?

Unit Price × Quantity = Total Amount per item

$0.23 × 12 = $2.76   Roberto should enter $2.76 in the purchase order for ink pens.

Enter this amount in the purchase order form.

Solve each problem and complete the purchase order form.

1. Find the amount Roberto should enter for the Black Markers.

   _____

2. Find the amount Roberto should enter for the Color Printer Cartridges.

   _____

3. If Computer Paper can be purchased at $5.36 per box, how many boxes did Roberto order for $21.44?

   _____

4. Roberto ordered 5 boxes of paper clips for a total cost of $4.15. What is the unit price per box?

   _____

5. What is the Total Purchase amount for the purchase order?

   _____

Holt Middle School Math   Course 2

Career Math
Proportional Reasoning

Environmental Scientist

What They Do

Environmental scientists conduct research to identify pollutants to reduce or eliminate the sources of these pollutants, which affect people, wildlife, and their environments. They observe, analyze and report measurements of pollutants in the air, water, soil, and other sources in order to make recommendations on how best to clean and preserve the environment. They often use their skills and knowledge to design and monitor waste disposal sites, as well as to plan and implement ways to preserve supplies and reclaim contaminated land and water to comply with Federal environmental regulations.

The Degree Required

A Bachelor's degree in environmental science, geological engineering, or geology; A Master's degree is required for most entry-level research positions in colleges, federal agencies, and state geological surveys; A Ph.D. is necessary for most high-level research positions.

Math Courses Needed

Algebra, geometry, calculus, economics and statistics

Other Courses Needed

Courses in biology, geology, hazardous waste management, environmental toxicology, chemistry, political science, ecology and physics are required.

How They Use Math

Environmental scientists use math when calculating the amount of pollutants in the environment. They collect samples and measure the amount of pollutant found in a specific amount of sample. They incorporate the use of mathematical ratios and proportions to determine the actual level of contaminant in the environment. When environmental scientists are performing experiments, they use equations to determine the concentration of particular solutions and reagents. They utilize statistics when conducting research and developing recommendations for environmental improvements.

Holt Middle School Math   Course 2

Career Math

Proportional Reasoning, continued

In March 1989, 11.2 million gallons of oil spilt into Alaska's Prince William Sound as a result of an oil tanker accident. Nearly 10,000 square miles were affected by the spill, including a national forest, wildlife refuges, and game sanctuaries.

A 2,000 ml water sample taken from a contaminated lake contained 0.9 ml of oil by-products. What is amount of oil by-product in the 300,000-gallon lake?

$$\frac{0.9\ ml}{2,000\ ml} = \frac{x\ gallons}{300,000\ gallons}$$ Write the proportion.

$$2,000x = 0.9 \cdot 300,000$$ Set the cross products equal.

$$\frac{2,000x}{2,000} = \frac{270,000}{2,000}$$ Divide each side by 2,000 to isolate the variable.

$$x = 135\ gallons$$

There is about 135 gallons of oil by-product in the lake.

Write a proportion for each problem. Solve.

1. To clean up beaches affected by the oil spill, environmental scientists used fertilizer to promote growth of microscopic bacteria that eat the hydrocarbons in the oil. This process is known as **bioremediation.** If the scientists deposited 2,500 mg of bacteria for every 25 square yards, how much bacteria did they use for 1,000 square yards?

2. For every seabird carcass found by the oil clean up crew, scientist predicted 7 times more seabirds had probably died. If clean up crews found 35,000 dead seabirds, how many did the scientists record as dying?

3. Reaching collection sites to obtain data was often difficult for the scientists because of the terrain. If a scientist had to climb a steep cliff he needed to insert a camming device into the cliff every 12 feet. This was to protect him in case of a fall. If a cliff was 119 feet high, how many camming devices did the scientist use? (Round up to the nearest whole number.)

Holt Middle School Math   Course 2

LESSON	**Consumer Math**
5-1	*Unit Pricing*

Wholesale clubs are very popular with today's consumer. The term **wholesale** means that the store is in the business of buying goods in quantity at discounted prices, usually direct from manufacturers or distributors, in order to sell them to the consumer. Typically, consumers can purchase the products they need at cheaper prices if they are willing to buy large quantities. The best way to determine the amount of savings is to calculate the **unit price** of the items purchased at the wholesale club and compare it to the retail unit price.

You purchase an 8-roll bundle of paper towels from a wholesale club. The cost for the bundle was $15.95. You could purchase 2 rolls of the same brand of paper towels at your local grocery store for $4.28. To determine which is the better value, you calculate the unit price for each purchase.

$\dfrac{\$15.95}{8 \text{ rolls}} = \$1.99$ per roll   wholesale unit price

$\dfrac{\$4.28}{2 \text{ rolls}} = \$2.14$ per roll   retail unit price

The paper towels at the wholesale club are a better value.

Solve.

1. Joel purchased a 60-oz box of his favorite cereal at a wholesale club for $12.59. Find the unit price of the cereal.

_____

2. With a coupon, Joel could purchase 20 oz of the same cereal for $3.99 at the grocery store. Which is the better value?

_____

3. Liz needs to purchase a set of 4 tires. The price at the wholesale club is $175, including installation. What is the unit price of the tires?

_____

4. The tire store's price was $50 per tire including installation. How much did Liz save by buying 4 tires at the wholesale club?

_____

5. Marta buys a 32 oz. bottle of shampoo at the wholesale club for $11.96. Find the unit price of the shampoo.

_____

6. At the salon, the same shampoo costs $6.95 for 12 oz. Which shampoo is the better value?

_____

     Holt Middle School Math   Course 2

LESSON 5-4 Consumer Math
Gas Mileage

When planning to purchase a new automobile, one factor to consider is the car's gas mileage. **Gas mileage,** listed as miles per gallon or mpg, is the number of miles the car runs for each gallon of gas. Automotive manufactures provide information on gas mileage for each model of automobile they produce. In fact, it is listed right on the sticker price of the car in big bold letters.

Suppose you want to buy a new car that averages 16 mpg on the highway. Because of your commute to work, you will be driving the car about 600 miles per week. Determine your cost per week to drive this car if the average price for gasoline is $1.59 per gallon.

Find the number of gallons you need to travel 600 miles.

$$600 \text{ miles} \cdot \frac{1 \text{ gallon}}{16 \text{ miles}} = 37.5 \text{ gallons}$$

Multiply the number of gallons by the price of gasoline.

$$37.5 \text{ gallons} \cdot \frac{\$1.59}{\text{gallon}} = \$59.63$$

It will cost you about $60 per week to drive your car.

Solve.

1. Marco's drove his economy car, which gets 44 mpg on the highway, 396 miles to visit his family. He paid $1.29 per gallon of gasoline each time he needed gas. How much did he spend in gasoline?

2. Hans wants to buy a new car that averages 18 mpg in the city. He plans to drive the car about 225 miles per week. How many gallons of gas per week will Hans use?

3. Gabby drives her car 300 miles per week. Each week she uses 20 gallons of gas. What kind of gas mileage does her car get?

4. If Gabby pays an average of $1.39 per gallon of gasoline, about how much per week does it cost to drive her car?

5. Which vehicle would be cheaper to take on a 350-mile round trip, your car that gets 12 mpg or a $60 rental car that gets 45 mpg? Gas is $1.43 per gallon.

Career Math
Percents

Human Resource Professionals

What They Do
Human resource professionals are responsible for attracting the most qualified employees and matching them to the jobs for which they are best suited. Additionally, they consult with top executives regarding strategic planning, leadership issues, and policy changes. They facilitate the effective use of employee skills by providing training opportunities and are involved in employee satisfaction initiatives.

Smaller organizations typically utilize human resource generalists who handle all aspects of human resources work, requiring a broad range of knowledge. In larger corporations, the top human resource executive usually develops and coordinates personnel programs and policies. A director or manager of human resources and, in some cases, a director of industrial relations, implements these policies.

The Degree Required
A Bachelor's degree in human resources, personnel administration, or industrial and labor relations

Math Courses Needed
Algebra, business mathematics, statistics and economics

Other Courses Needed
Most prospective human resource specialists should take courses in compensation, recruitment, training and development, and performance appraisal, as well as courses in principles of management, organizational structure, and industrial psychology. Courses in labor law, collective bargaining, labor economics, labor history, and industrial psychology provide a valuable background for the prospective labor relations' specialist.

How They Use Math
Human resource professionals incorporate statistical knowledge when conducting employee satisfaction surveys, developing performance improvement plans, and in succession planning. Additionally, compensation specialists rely heavily on their knowledge of math in developing compensation and budget plans and proposals.

Holt Middle School Math **Course 2**

CHAPTER	**Career Math**
6	*Percents, continued*

Terrence is a human resource professional who specializes in compensation. Every year Terrence has to establish a salary increase procedure for the employees of the company. Typically, the company sets aside a percentage of its annual budget to allow for increases in the employees' salaries.

Terrence works for a manufacturing company with an annual operating budget of $1,000,000. This year he budgeted that he would need 10% of the annual operating budget for salary increases. How much money will Terrence have to allocate to salary increases?

$\$1,000,000 \cdot \dfrac{10}{100} = \$100,000$ Change 10% to a fraction. Multiply.

Terrence will have $100,000 to allocate for salary increases.

Usually as part of an annual review, an employee is given a **raise,** an increase in salary, as a percentage of his current salary. For example, an employee makes $30,000 per year and is given a 5% raise at his annual review. How much is his raise? How much is his new salary?

$\$30,000 \cdot \dfrac{5}{100} = \$1,500$ Change 5% to a fraction. Multiply.

The new salary equals: Salary + Raise = New Salary
$\qquad\qquad\qquad\quad \$30,000 + \$1,500 = \$31,500$

The employee received a raise of $1,500. His new salary is $31,500.

Solve.

1. A company with an annual operating budget of $2,000,000 set aside 15% for salary increases. What amount did they set aside for salary increases?

2. Shauna is scheduled to receive her annual salary increase next month. Her current salary is $42,000 per year. Calculate the amount of her raise, and her new salary if she gets a 7% raise.

3. Molly earns $7.00 per hour at the paper mill. At her annual review she was told that she would receive a $0.35 per hour increase in pay. What percent increase did she receive?

4. The operating budget for your company is $2,500,000 per year. The company budgeted $300,000 for salary increases. What percent is budgeted for salary increases?

Holt Middle School Math   Course 2

Name _____ Date _____ Class _____

Consumer Math

Sales Tax

In the United States, most states have a general sales tax. State **sales tax** rates vary from state to state. **Sales taxes** are taxes on retail merchandise and are collected at the point of sale by the retailer. Taxation is used as a way to raise money to finance the government. Governments use tax revenues to pay soldiers and police, to build dams and roads, to operate schools and hospitals, to provide food to the poor and medical care for the elderly, as well as many other purposes. Without taxes to fund its activities, government could not exist. Taxation is the most important source of revenues for modern governments and typically accounts for 90 percent or more of their income.

Vinnie purchased a hat and a pair of socks. The sales tax on his purchase was $0.84. What percent sales tax was he charged?

Shirt	$15.50	Pants	$22.75
Hat	$7.50	Skirt	$24.50
Pair of Socks	$4.50	Boots	$29.00
Scarf	12.00	Shoes	$21.75

Find the cost of the purchase: $7.50 + 4.50 = $12.00.

$12x = 0.84$ Set up an equation.

$\dfrac{12x}{12} = \dfrac{0.84}{12}$ Divide both sides by 12 to isolate x.

$x = 0.07 = 7\%$ Divide. Convert the decimal to a percent.

Vinnie was charged a 7% sales tax rate.

Use the table above to answer each question.

1. Steve purchased a shirt, a pair of pants and a scarf. He is charged $52.76 for his purchase. What is the sales tax rate, to the nearest whole number?

   _____

2. Lisa bought a pair of boots and a pair of shoes. The sales tax on her purchase was $2.79. What percent sales tax did she pay?

   _____

3. Gloria bought 2 shirts and 3 pair of pants. The sales tax is 4.5%. How much did she pay in sales tax?

   _____

4. Sam purchased 2 scarves. He paid $1.20 in sales tax. What percent sales tax did he pay?

   _____

     Holt Middle School Math   **Course 2**

Consumer Math

| LESSON |
| 6-6 | *Simple Interest*

When money is borrowed or invested, **interest** is charged or earned for the use of that money for a certain period of time. The amount of interest depends on the interest rate, the **principal,** or amount of money borrowed or invested, and the length of time of the loan or investment. This type of interest is referred to as **simple interest.**

The formula for finding simple interest is:

Interest = Principal • Rate • Time or $I = P • R • T$

Calculate the simple interest on a $100 loan borrowed for 2 years at a 10% interest rate. Then find the total amount of money paid back to the bank.

$I = P • R • T$ Write the formula.
$I = 100 • 0.10 • 2$ Substitute known values. Convert the percent to a decimal.
$I = \$20$ Multiply.

The simple interest on the loan is $20.

The total amount paid back to the bank is the principal plus interest.
$100 + $20 = $120.

You would pay the bank a total of $120 for borrowing $100 for 2 years.

Solve.

1. Marcy bought a washer from an appliance store for $625. Marcy financing the entire amount for 1 year at a 25% interest rate. How much interest will Marcy pay? Find the total amount she will pay for the washer.

2. Haley needs to borrow $1,000 to help pay for her tuition. A bank offers a loan at a rate of 8% for 3 years. How much interest will she pay for this loan? How much will she pay in total for the money?

3. Shawn invested $2,000 in a simple interest certificate of deposit, five years ago. The interest rate was 6% for 5 years. How much money did Shawn have at the end of the 5 years?

4. Barney loaned his nephew $5,500 to buy a used car. His nephew agreed to pay him back in 1 year. At the end of the year, the nephew had paid his uncle a total of $6,050. What interest rate did his uncle charge?

Holt Middle School Math   Course 2

Name _____ Date _____ Class _____

Architect

What They Do
Architects plan and design buildings and structures. Shopping malls, school campuses, airports, and downtown office areas all began as designs on an architect's drawing table. Some architects specialize in one kind of building design, such as homes, commercial buildings, sports arenas, theatres, churches, or even factories. Architects are often hired to redesign an existing structure.

Architects must be familiar with local and state building regulations including plumbing, heating, and ventilation codes as well as being knowledgeable in many areas of building and construction processes.

The Degree Required
A five-year bachelor's degree in architecture from a liberal arts college is required for this career. In addition, all states require architects to be registered, or licensed, in the state where they work. To receive a license a person must have an architecture degree plus 3 years experience, and must pass the Architect Registration Examination.

Math Courses Needed
Algebra, geometry, plane geometry, and trigonometry

Other Courses Needed
Architects need to complete coursework in economics, drafting, art and business. It is also helpful to be versed in CADD, Computer Aided Drafting and Design.

How They Use Math
Architects use geometry daily, as every structure is comprised of shapes, angles, lines, and curves. Trigonometry and geometry are applied to measurements and angles to complete an accurate drawing. Architects apply construction methods and engineering principles to their work to visually convey their design to the client.

Holt Middle School Math   Course 2

CHAPTER	**Career Math**
7	*Plane Figures, continued*

An architect has the freedom to design with his artistic intuition. For instance, when putting a roof on a building or a home he can create a different visual affect, depending on the angle. A 180° roofline is flat, where as a 60° roofline is very steep. The ridge is the uppermost, horizontal external angle formed by the intersection of two sloping roof planes. Typically, the more rooflines on a house or building, and the steeper the roof, the more costly it is to construct. An architect's design might be guided by cost, but it also needs to be aesthetically pleasing to the eye.

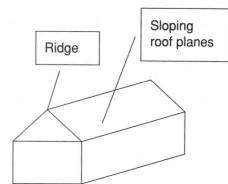

A ridge with a 30° angle is formed by two sloping roof planes of equal measure. What is the angle measure of each plane? What type of triangle is formed?

Use the fact that the sum of the angles in a triangle equal 180°.

$30 + x + x = 180$	Set up the equation.
$30 + 2x = 180$	Add like terms.
$2x = 150$	Subtract 30 from both sides.
$x = 75$	Divide each side by 2 to isolate x.

Each plane measures 75°. Since two sides have equal measures, the triangle formed is an isosceles triangle.

Solve.

1. The angle of a roof ridge is designed to be 60°. The slope of the roof planes is shown to be the same on both sides of the ridge. The architect forgot to write down the angle measures on the drawing. What are the two missing angles? What type of triangle is formed?

2. The angle of a roof ridge was designed to be 75°, but the customer wants the architect to change it to 90°. The architect insists that the structure needs to have the slope of the roof plane angles equal. What is the angle of each roof plane? What type of triangle is formed?

3. The angles at the roofline of your aunt's house are 75° and 15°. What is the angle in the ridge? What type of triangle is formed?

4. The angles at the roofline of a new house are 70° and 50°. What is the angle in the ridge? What type of triangle is formed?

Holt Middle School Math   Course 2

Name _____ Date _____ Class _____

Consumer Math
Toll Bridges

Bridges are strategically constructed for the purpose of permitting passage over water, land, and roads. Because of the expense of bridge construction and maintenance, some bridges charge a **toll,** a fee or payment, for the right or privilege to use it.

For the 2-lane bridge that connects the main land to the island in Ocean Park, a toll is charged. The table below shows the toll fees.

Type of Vehicle	Toll
Car	$0.50
SUV	$0.75
Camper or Trailer	$2.00
Semi Truck	$4.50

Use the chart and the picture of the bridge for each exercise.

1. About how much toll is collected in one week if an average of 200 cars cross the bridge per day?

_____

2. Are the columns of the bridge parallel or perpendicular to the water below the bridge?

_____

3. Do the columns of the bridge appear to make a 45°, 60°, or 90° angle with the base of the bridge?

_____

4. To bring supplies to the island, a truck comes to and from the island every day. How much does the truck pay in tolls for a 30-day period?

_____

5. Are the 2-lanes on the bridge parallel or perpendicular to each other?

_____

6. What angle measure do the 2-lanes make with each other?

_____

7. Some toll bridges, like the one shown, are over water. As a boat passes under the bridge, the drawbridge rises up so the boat can clear. If a flat drawbridge, parallel to the water, rises the center section to 70°, what angle does this section now make with the road?

_____

8. The drawbridge in Exercise 7 charges a $15 toll to let a boat pass underneath it. On average, 75 boats per week pass under the bridge. How much money is collected in tolls per week? As a boat passes under the bridge, is it parallel or perpendicular to the road above it?

_____

Holt Middle School Math   **Course 2**

CHAPTER 7-4	Consumer Math
	Budgets

A circle graph can be used to show the estimated weekly operating budget for a local grocery store. A **budget** is a systematic plan for meeting expenses in a given time period.

The circle graph shows the estimated operating budget for a typical week.

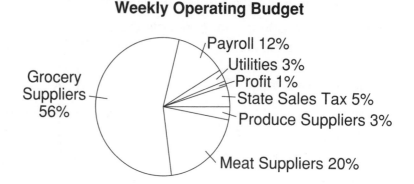

Weekly Operating Budget

Payroll 12%
Utilities 3%
Profit 1%
State Sales Tax 5%
Produce Suppliers 3%
Grocery Suppliers 56%
Meat Suppliers 20%

Approximately 3% of the weekly income must be budgeted for utilities, such as electric, gas, and water. What is the central angle measure of this sector on the circle graph?

The angular measure of a circle is 360°. Since the sector for utilities is 3% of the graph, then the central angle is 3% of the circle's angular measure.

3% of 360° = 0.03 × 360° = 10.8°

The central angle measure of the utility sector is 10.8°.

Use the circle graph above for each exercise.

1. What accounts for the largest weekly expense of the grocery store?

2. What is the central angle measure of the sector from Exercise 1?

3. Which sector of the graph is a little less than 90°?

4. What is the actual central angle measure of the sector from Exercise 3?

5. How much of the budget is designated for payroll expense?

6. What central angle measure is used to show the amount budgeted for payroll expense?

Name _____ Date _____ Class _____

Career Math

Perimeter, Circumference, and Area

Construction Manager

What They Do
Construction managers plan and direct construction projects. They typically define the scope of the project and create the initial project estimate. Construction managers evaluate various construction methods and determine the most cost-effective plan and schedule. They schedule all required construction site activities into logical, specific steps, and budget the time required to meet established deadlines. They oversee the performance of all trade contractors and are responsible for ensuring all work is completed on schedule.

The Degree Required
A Bachelor's of Science degree in Construction Management

Math Courses Needed
Algebra, geometry, trigonometry and calculus

Other Courses Needed
A construction manager should take courses in engineering, CADD-computer aided drawing and design, estimating, physics, chemistry, and business management.

How They Use Math
A construction manager uses math to estimate the type and amount of construction materials needed for every phase of the project. They use their knowledge of measurement, scale ratios, geometry, and trigonometry to interpret construction blueprints and architectural drawings. They also use spreadsheets and scheduling programs to track a project's schedule and budget.

Holt Middle School Math   Course 2

Career Math

8 *Perimeter, Circumference, and Area, continued*

A construction manager needs to fence in a job site to prevent unauthorized entry into the hardhat or construction area. The building being constructed measures 1,600 feet by 2,880 feet. The manager needs to leave 135 feet on each side of the building for adequate space to work.

To determine how much fence he needs, find the perimeter of the construction site.

$2(1,600 + 135 + 135) \bullet 2(2,880 + 135 + 135) = 10,040$ ft

The construction manager needs to order 10,040 feet of fence.

Solve.

1. A construction site measures 600 yards on all 4 sides. Find the perimeter of the site.

2. What is the perimeter of a construction site that measures 185 ft by 227 ft?

3. A trucking company is constructing a facility close to the highway. The facility will be in the shape of a polygon with 4 unequal sides. The sides will measure $\frac{1}{2}$ mile, $\frac{2}{5}$ mile, $\frac{1}{4}$ mile and $\frac{1}{5}$ mile. Find the perimeter of the facility.

4. Construction on a new aquatic center is scheduled to begin next month. The shape of the construction site is a regular pentagon, with each side measuring 500 feet. Find the perimeter of the site.

5. Before a building can be constructed, the construction manager schedules the footers of the building to be poured. The base of the building measures 500 m x 435 m. Find the area of the base of the building.

6. A circular fountain is being renovated at Southsea Park. The fountain has a 24-ft diameter. The construction manager fences in the area around the fountain to prevent unauthorized entry into the site. The diameter of the fenced area is 40 ft. Find the area of the construction site.

Consumer Math
Water Consumption

In Alex's community, water is billed according to the number of monthly gallons of water used.

Water Usage Chart

Gallons Used	Cost
first 2,000 gallons	$12.50
remaining gallons	$4.75 per 1,000 gallons

Alex's family uses 4,000 quarts of water every month washing dishes. What is the cost of this water consumption?

$$4,000 \text{ quarts} \cdot \frac{1 \text{ gallon}}{4 \text{ quarts}} = 1,000 \text{ gallons}$$ There are 4 quarts in 1 gallon.

The water usage cost Alex's family $12.50

Solve. Use the information above.

1. In one month Eric used 1,200 gallons of water washing his cars and 2,000 quarts of water running his faucets. How many total gallons of water did Eric use?

2. In one month Rick used 3,000 gallons of water watering his yard and 3,000 quarts of water running his washing machine. How many total gallons of water did Rick use?

_____

3. Determine Eric's water usage bill from Exercise 1.

4. Determine Rick's water usage bill from Exercise 2.

_____

5. A town gives a once a year pool credit of 39,400 quarts. A pool credit allows people to fill their pool and not pay charges on the water needed to fill it. Chuck used 18,560 gallons of water in May plus an additional 11,400 gallons to fill his pool.

   a. How many gallons of water can Chuck claim as a pool credit?

_____

   b. How many gallons of water will Chuck be billed for the month of May? (Deduct the pool credit.) What is the amount of his water bill?

_____

Consumer Math

CHAPTER 8-4 *Price Comparison*

When working on a home improvement project, it is best to get a good value on the materials you need to purchase. The table lists the price of floor tiles.

Type Tile	Single Price	Box Price
Vinyl (12-inch square)	$1.45	$35.00 per box of 30
Ceramic (6-inch square)	$0.75	$18.00 per box of 28
Ceramic (12-inch square)	$2.50	$35.00 per box of 15

The floor you need to cover is 9 ft by 9 ft. If you use the 6-inch ceramic tiles, should you buy tiles by the box or a combination of each?

Find the area of the floor.
9 feet × 9 feet = 81 square feet

Find the number of tiles needed. You will need 4 tiles for each square foot.
81 square feet × 4 = 324 tiles

Find the number of boxes of tiles.

Number of boxes = $\frac{324}{28}$ = 11.6 boxes. Round to 12 full boxes.

Find the cost if buying only full boxes of tiles.
12 boxes × $18 = $216
Find the cost if buying a combination of each.
(11 boxes × $18) + (16 tiles × $0.75) = $210

Buying a combination of boxes and individual tiles is the better buy.

Use the information above for each excercise.

1. If you decided to install the 12-inch ceramic tiles, how many boxes and individual tiles would you need?

2. What is the cost for the tiles in Exercise 1?

3. You found the same 12-inch ceramic tile for $25 per box at a discount store. You can only purchase full boxes. What is the tile cost?

4. The vinyl tile is not as decorative but it is easier to install. What is the best buy, boxes of tiles or individual tiles for the floor? What is the cost?

Holt Middle School Math   Course 2

Name _____ Date _____ Class _____

Career Math

Geometry: Volume and Surface Area

Restaurateur

What They Do
A restaurateur is an owner of a restaurant. Because of the demands of the industry, restaurateurs are typically hard working committed people. On a daily basis, restaurateurs estimate food consumption, place food orders, schedule and check deliveries, deal with customers and employees, coordinate waste removal and pest control, and arrange for equipment maintenance and repairs.

Restaurateurs also work closely with their head chef in selecting successful menu items. This decision is based on the likely number of customers and past popularity of dishes. Other menu selection issues include minimizing waste, the need for variety and seasonal availability of foods, determining costs, and assigning prices.

The Degree Required
A Bachelor's or Associate Degree in hotel restaurant or food service management

Math Courses Needed
General math, business math, probability, statistics, and regression analysis

Other Courses Needed
Food service, nutrition, sanitation, accounting, finance, economics, and business law

How They Use Math
Statistical data on past sales can aid in compiling the probability of future sales. Regression analysis might be used to identify how sales of specific menu items correlate to price, season, day of the week, or other factors. Basic and business math is critical in calculating food, labor, and overhead costs.

Holt Middle School Math   Course 2

CHAPTER 9 **Career Math**

Geometry: Volume and Surface Area, *continued*

Bill is the new owner of an oceanside restaurant. He hopes 50% of his total profits can be realized from beverage sales. His basic glassware is shaped like a cylinder and comes in two sizes. Bill wants to know how much each glass holds, and the beverage cost to fill each glass before setting his prices. The smaller glass has a 1.5-inch radius and is 6.5 inches tall. The larger glass has a 2.75-inch radius and is 8 inches tall. Bill's average beverage cost is $0.02 per cubic inch. What is the cost to fill each sized glass?

Volume of a cylinder $= \pi r^2 h$
Volume of smaller glass $= 3.14 \times 1.5^2 \times 6.5 \approx 46 \ in^3$
Volume of larger glass $= 3.14 \times 2.75^2 \times 8 \approx 190 \ in^3$

Total Beverage Cost $=$ Volume $\times$ Cost per cubic inch
Cost of smaller glass $= 46 \ in^3 \times \$0.02 = \$0.92$
Cost of larger glass $= 190 \ in^3 \times \$0.02 = \$3.80$

Solve.

1. Bill wants to offer another beverage size midway between his current glass sizes described above. He can choose from one of these options:
A) radius 1.75 in., height 6.75 in.
B) radius 2 in., height 7 in.
C) radius 2.25 in., height 7.25 in.
Which glass size should Bill purchase? What will it cost to fill the glass?

2. At the carryout window on the oceanside of the restaurant, Bill sells spherically shaped popcorn balls in two sizes. One ball is 4 inches in diameter the other ball size is 5 inches in diameter. Bill's cost for the popcorn is $0.015 per cubic inch popped. What is the volume, to the nearest cubic inch of each popcorn ball? What is Bill's cost for each?

3. For July 4th, Bill wants to put special lettering on his largest cylindrical plastic cups. The cups have a 2-inch radius and are 7 inches tall. The cost, per hundred cups, to apply the lettering is $10 for lateral surface areas of 50 in^2 to 75 in^2, and $15 for 76 in^2 to 100 in^2. What will be Bill's cost for 100 cups?

4. Bill wants to build a large aquarium in the entryway to his restaurant. The fish store owner next door will maintain the aquarium for $10 per cubic foot per month. If the aquarium is a rectangular prism 6 feet long, 1.5 feet wide, and 3 feet high, what will be Bill's monthly maintenance bill?

Name _____ Date _____ Class _____

Consumer Math

Shopping for Supplies

Decorative ceramic globes are currently a popular item. Spherical globes are painted with special paint and then covered with a decorative glaze. The cost to make the globes depends on the size of the globe and amount of paint needed to cover its surface.

Shari wants to make ten decorative ceramic globes to sell at a market. She needs to determine how much paint she will need to paint two coats of paint on each of ten 4-inch diameter globes. The paint comes in quart containers that cover 100 square feet.

Find the surface area of a 4-inch globe: $S = 4\pi r^2 = 4 \times 3.14 \times 2^2 = 50.24\ in^2$
Find the surface area for 10 globes: $10 \times 50.24\ in^2 = 502.4\ in^2$
Calculate amount of paint, two coats per globe: $502.4 \times 2 = 1{,}004.8\ in^2$

A quart of paint covers $100\ ft^2$. Convert this to square inches.

$$100\ ft^2 \times \frac{144\ in^2}{1\ ft^2} = 14{,}400\ in^2$$

The area for 10 globes is $1{,}004.8\ in^2$, so one quart of paint is needed.

Solve. Use the information given above if necessary.

1. Jamal wants to make as many 5-inch diameter globes, with two coats of paint per globe, as possible. How many globes can be painted from one quart of paint?

_____

2. The specialty paint for ceramic globes costs $12 per quart. With two coats of paint for each globe, what is the per globe cost to paint each of the 5-inch globes from Exercise 1?

_____

3. Alyce is making one hundred 5-inch globes. She plans to use a paint that requires only one coat but costs $20 per quart. Which paint is the most economical, the $20 or the $12 per quart?

_____

4. Another popular craft project is painting wooden boxes with lids. Find the surface area of a wooden box that measures 12 in. × 10 in. × 6 in.

_____

5. How many quarts of paint are needed to paint ten boxes in Exercise 4, inside and out, with two coats?

_____

6. Assume that the paint costs $12 per quart. Calculate the cost per box if Billy is painting 10 boxes.

_____

Holt Middle School Math   Course 2

CHAPTER	Consumer Math
9-5	*Packaging*

Sweet Things Candy and Nut Shoppe carry a variety of specialty candies and nuts. They package their product in both glass jars and decorative boxes. Pricing is based on the amount the container will hold of a particular product.

The best selling package of nuts is a 3 in. × 4 in. × 2 in. box that holds 6-oz of special blended mixed nuts. The owner recently decided to package the nuts in a box similar to the 6-oz box, but larger by a factor of 2. How many ounces of nuts will this new box hold?

New weight = old weight • (factor)^3
New weight = 6 oz • 2^3
New weight = 48 oz

The new box will hold 48 oz of nuts.

Solve.

1. The best selling box of candy at Sweet Things holds 10 ounces of candy. How many ounces of candy would a similar box hold if it were increased by a factor of 1.5?

2. If the wholesale cost of nuts for the 3 in. × 4 in. × 2 in. box is $0.75. How much will it cost to fill a 48 oz box with the same type of nuts?

3. The wholesale cost of a fancy nut mixture is $2 per pound. How many 3 in. × 4 in. × 2 in. boxes can be completely filled with 10 pounds of this mix?

4. The smallest cylindrical jar currently used to package candy has a $2\frac{1}{2}$ in. diameter and is 5 in. high. What is the volume of the next size jar if it is larger than the smaller jar by a factor of $1\frac{1}{2}$?

5. Gulf Coast Graphics has been hired to design a label for the $2\frac{1}{2}$ in. × 5 in. cylindrical jar. If the label is to come within 1 in. of the top of the jar, what is the surface area of the label?

6. How may full labels from Exercise 5 will Gulf Coast Graphics be able to get out of $8\frac{1}{2}$ in. × 14 in. paper stock?

Holt Middle School Math   Course 2

<table>
<tr><td>CHAPTER</td></tr>
<tr><td>10</td></tr>
</table>

Career Math
Probability

Food Service Manager

What They Do

Food service managers work in restaurants, hotels, and institutional food service facilities. They are responsible for selecting and pricing menu items, using food and supplies efficiently, and maintaining a high quality of food preparation and service. These managers also have many administrative responsibilities, including hiring and scheduling employees and ordering supplies needed to prepare and serve menu items. They must meet with suppliers to make sure inventory is available and maintained, and arrange for equipment repair and maintenance, waste removal, and pest control. Some managers in larger restaurants or hotels are responsible for arranging and planning banquets.

Degree Required

An Associate's or Bachelor's degree in restaurant and food service management or hotel/restaurant management

Math Courses Needed

Basic mathematics and business math

Other Courses Needed

Nutrition, food planning and preparation, accounting, business law, management, and computer science

How They Use Math

Food service managers use math to analyze recipes to determine food, labor, and overhead cost. Based on the findings of this analysis, the manager must determine and assign prices for each item on the menu. They are responsible for estimating food consumption to minimize waste. Some managers are responsible for calculating payroll, maintaining records of all purchases, and ensuring each account and supplier is paid on a regular basis. Finally, these managers must record data pertaining to the number, type, and cost of items sold to evaluate and discontinue menu items that may be unpopular or unprofitable.

Holt Middle School Math   Course 2

CHAPTER	**Career Math**
10	*Probability, continued*

Food Service Managers have many responsibilities from scheduling employees, to determining daily menu specials.

Gisha received a shipment of fresh flounder (F) and salmon (S) from her seafood supplier, and fresh green beans (G), snow peas (P), and asparagus (A) from her vegetable supplier. Given these items, how many combinations of entrées can she make so that each dish is served with a fish and vegetable?

FG FP FA   List all of the entrées that contain flounder (F).

SG SP SA   List all of the entrées that contain salmon (S).

There are 6 possible combinations of entrées.

Solve.

1. The restaurant that Henry manages offers a salad with every entrée. The customer can choose between a spinach salad or a chef salad and five different salad dressings. How many possible salad choices are there?

2. Dale likes to put vases of fresh flowers on each restaurant table. If each vase contains 2 of 5 different types of flowers, how many combinations of arrangements are possible?

3. Ralph needs to call his fish, meat, vegetable, and linen suppliers today. What is the probability that he calls his vegetable supplier first?

4. Mindy is expecting 4 waiters to arrive at the restaurant between noon and 1:00 P.M. In how many different orders might the waiters arrive?

5. For the past three weeks, Toni has been recording the sale of meatloaf. His records show that he sold more than 4 of these entrees 7 out of 21 days. What is the probability that he will sell more than 4 of these entrées on the 22nd day?

6. Greta found that on 20 out of the past 30 days the blackened swordfish was ordered at least 10 times per day. What is the probability that at least 10 customers will order it on the 31st day? Is this a big selling item?

Consumer Math

LESSON 10-1 *Home Warranties*

Many people who buy a home often purchase a **home warranty.**
These warranty contracts remove the worry associated with the
probability of something vital within the home breaking or failing
during the first year the home is owned.

Gene and Janice are purchasing a 15-year old home. They can buy
a home warranty for $325.00. They know that the average repair
cost for home systems is $345 and the probability of a system
breaking or failing is 33%. Find the probable annual cost of repairs
to determine if they should purchase the warranty.

$345 × 0.33 = $113.85   Multiply the average repair cost by the probability.

$113.85 < $325.00   It is probable that Gene and Janice would save $211.15
                          if they do not buy the home warranty.

Use the table for each exercise.

1. A home warranty costs $375.00. The new homeowner is worried about having to replace the furnace based on the results of the

Service	Average Replacement Cost	Probability of Occurrence
Central Heating/Cooling	$1,850.00	25%
Hot Water Tank	$225.00	30%
Dishwasher	$375.00	60%
Oven/Range	$995.00	40%

home inspection. Using the figures above, should the consumer purchase the warranty? Explain.

_____

2. The table above represents figures for homes that are older than 10 years. With newer homes, the probability of replacement drops. For example, the probability of an oven/range needing replacement decreases to 10%. Would it be favorable to purchase a $375 home warranty for a newer home? Explain.

_____

3. The new homeowner knows that the heating/cooling system and oven/range have been recently replaced. Would it still be wise to purchase a $375 home warranty?

_____

_____

Holt Middle School Math   Course 2

LESSON 10-6 Consumer Math
Grocery Budget

Many families who are on a strict household budget must carefully plan meals and shop wisely. To stay within a grocery budget and purchase as many food items as possible, the conscientious shopper may search for sales, buy store brands, or clip coupons. Others may attempt to buy in bulk from wholesale clubs and divide the merchandise into required serving sizes.

Mandy purchased chicken (C), steak (S), noodles (N), potatoes (P), green beans (G) and broccoli (B). How many different combinations of meals can she make if she serves a meat, a starch (noodles or potatoes), and a vegetable with each meal?

CNG, CNB, CPG, CNB   List all of the meals that begin with chicken.

SNG, SNB, SPG, SNB   List all of the meals that begin with steak.

There is a total of 8 combinations of meals that Mandy can make.

Solve.

1. Mary purchased several cuts of beef (B) when the grocery store was having a big sale. She also bought sweet potatoes (P), squash (S), rice (R), and carrots (C). If she prepares the beef with 2 side dishes, how many combinations of meals can she make?

2. Rachel bought some "snack" items to put in her children's lunch bags. She bought carrot sticks (C), yogurt (Y), raisins (R), apples (A), and grapes (G). She will include 2 different snacks with each lunch. How many different combinations can she make with what she purchased?

3. Pasta is a big hit in the Salvi household. Mrs. Salvi tries to be creative by adding different items to the pasta. This week she bought tomatoes (T), chicken (C), broccoli (B), and garlic (G). How many combinations can she make by combining the pasta with one other ingredient? Three ingredients?

4. When summer fruits are on sale, Greta likes to make fruit salad. She can choose from watermelon, cantaloupe, strawberries, peaches, kiwi, berries, and honeydew. If she combines 2 of these fruits with watermelon, how many combinations of fruit salad can she make?

Name _____ Date _____ Class _____

Market Research Analyst

What They Do

Market research analysts are responsible for examining the potential sales of a product or service. They advise companies on the promotion, distribution, design and pricing of products or services. Market analysts may also determine if it is wise for a company to add new lines of product, open new branches/stores, or diversify the company's operations.

The Degree Required

Most positions require a graduate degree in economics, business administration, marketing, or statistics.

Math Courses Needed

Statistics and business math

Other Courses Needed

Economics, business, marketing, psychology, sociology, and computer science

How They Use Math

Marketing analysts use math to analyze and interpret statistical data on past sales to predict future sales. They design methods for gathering data on competitors, and they analyze prices, sales, and methods of marketing and distribution. After generating data, market research analysts evaluate it through statistical operations and make recommendations to their clients in the form of a detailed report. Since these recommendations impact a company's future financial state, it is important that the market research analysts' data, analysis, and interpretation be accurate and thorough.

Holt Middle School Math Course 2

11 *Multistep Equations and Inequalities, continued*

A market research analyst collects data to determine consumer preference, the sales of particular products, and public attitude. After the data is collected, the analyst evaluates it and interprets it to look for trends and then make recommendations.

A market research analyst is hired to help a political leader determine public support on an important issue. After designing a survey and collecting data from 1,300 people, the analyst found that twice as many women than men support the issue. If 600 people support the issue, how many are women and how many are men?

Let x = the number of men. So $2x$ = the number of women.

$x + 2x = 600$	Write an algebraic equation.
$3x = 600$	Add like terms.
$\dfrac{3x}{3} = \dfrac{600}{3}$	Solve for x.
$x = 200$	200 men support the issue.
$2x = 400$	400 women support the issue.

Solve.

1. A market research analyst was hired to determine which flavor of yogurt people in a certain area preferred. The analyst collected data from 2,000 people and found that people preferred Brand A three times as much than Brand B. How many people preferred Brand A? Brand B?

_____

2. Data was collected to investigate the sales of a particular type of snow ski. Sales over 3 years totaled $637,000. Sales were 4 times as much in the first year than the third year and twice as much in the second year from the third year. What were the total sales for each year?

_____

3. A market research analyst is trying to determine if a franchise should be opened in a particular area. He found that four times as many people stated they would shop at the store than those who would not. If 1,500 people were surveyed, how many people said they would shop at the store?

_____

4. A market research analyst found that in a recent presidential election, 10% of the votes came from the West Coast, 25% from the Northeast, 20% from the Midwest, and 9 million votes came from the South. What was the total number of votes? How many votes came from the Midwest?

_____

Consumer Math

What's a Dollar Worth?

Jordan wants to know how much a dollar today will be worth a year from now. In other words, she wants to know the **present value** of the dollar. The value of a dollar is affected by the **interest rate.** As interest rates rise, the present value of future dollars will fall, and when interest rates drop, the present value of the dollar held in the future will increase.

How much will $100 today be worth in terms of dollars you will have one year from now if the interest rate is 7% (0.07)?

The present value of a dollar is calculated as follows:

$F = \frac{1}{1+r}(T)$ Where r = interest rate, F = future dollars, and T = todays dollars.

$F = \frac{1}{1 + 0.07}(100)$ Substitute 0.07 for r, and 100 for T.

$F = 0.93 \times 100$
$F = \$93.00$

So, $100 now will only be worth $93 in one year.

Solve.

1. If the interest rate is 5% (0.05), how much will $1,000 paid to you today be worth a year from now?

   _____

2. If the interest rate is 8% (0.08), what is the present value of $2,500 paid to you a year from now?

   _____

3. What is the future value of $25 paid to you today if the interest rate is 12% (0.12)?

   _____

4. What is the future value of $25 paid to you today if the interest rate is 3% (0.03)?

   _____

5. If the interest rate is 6% (0.06), how much will $45,000 be worth one year from now?

   _____

6. If interest rates drop to 2%, will $45,000 be worth more or less than when the interest rate is 6%?

   _____

Consumer Math

LESSON 11-2 *What Do You Owe?*

Almost all business owners require legal services to review and prepare documents, transactions, and various other legal matters. Lawyers usually charge businesses a base fee plus an hourly rate based on a **minimum billing time.** This means that if a legal service, such as a phone call made on your behalf, lasts for 2 minutes and your minimum billing time is $\frac{1}{10}$ hour (six minutes), you will be charged $\frac{1}{10}$ of the lawyer's hourly rate.

To determine the actual cost of legal expenses you need to know the minimum billable time and the lawyer's hourly rate. Find the amount a client owes for a meeting with his lawyer based on a base fee of $40, plus an additional hourly rate of $150, billed on a quarter-hour (15 minutes) basis.

Service	Base Fee	Minimum Billing Time	Hourly Rate	Actual Time Spent	Amount Due
Client Meeting	$40	$\frac{1}{4}$ hour	$150 per hour	38 minutes	?

Since the minimum billing time is every quarter of an hour, round up the actual time entry to the next 15-minute increment, 45 minutes. Multiply the total billable time, in hours, by the hourly rate and then add it to the base fee to determine the total amount of the bill.

$$\left(\frac{45}{60} \cdot 150\right) + 40 = 152.50 \qquad \text{Change minutes to hours.}$$

So, the client owes $152.50 for legal services.

Complete the table.

	Service	Base Fee	Minimum Billing Time	Hourly Rate	Actual Time Spent	Amount Due
1.	Letter writing	$35	$\frac{1}{4}$ hour	$100 per hour	22 minutes	
2.	Court appearance	$75	$\frac{1}{4}$ hour	$150 per hour	54 minutes	
3.	Meeting with prosecutor	$60	$\frac{1}{10}$ hour	$90 per hour	40 minutes	
4.	Meeting notes	$50	$\frac{1}{10}$ hour	$90 per hour	16 minutes	

Holt Middle School Math   Course 2

CHAPTER	**Career Math**
12	*Graphs and Functions*

Statistician

What They Do
Statisticians use the scientific application of mathematical principles in the collection, analysis, and interpretation of data. The work of statisticians is applied in many areas including biology, economics, engineering, medicine, public health, government, marketing, education, sports, and engineering.

The Degree Required
A Master's degree in statistics or mathematics is usually the minimal educational requirement. Research and academic positions require a doctoral degree in statistics.

Math Courses Needed
Statistics, calculus, differential equations, vector analysis, mathematical modeling, and probability theory

Other Coursed Needed
Depending on the applied field in which the individual pursues, courses in biology, economics, education, engineering, business, and psychology should be taken. A strong background in computer science is recommended since computers are widely used for statistical applications.

How They Use Math
Statisticians use mathematical principles to design surveys and experiments, to collect, process, and analyze data, and to interpret and summarize results.

CHAPTER	**Career Math**
12	*Graphs and Functions, continued*

A statistician is responsible for analyzing and interpreting data in many situations. Statisticians must use a variety of statistical equations and functions to help them to predict future events. Statisticians study the functional relationship between cause and effect. The effect that certain inputs have on a measured output is modeled using mathematical formulas.

For example, a statistician working in the government's agricultural department may want to find out how to best improve tomato farmers' yields. Experimental data from a leading agricultural university found the following data from using different amounts of fertilizer on a popular tomato plant.

Experimental Results

Tons of fertilizer used per acre, t	0	1	5	7	9	10	15	20
Number of tomatoes produced per acre, y	1,500	1,600	2,000	2,200	2,400	2,500	3,000	3,500

Use the table above to solve.

1. How many tomatoes are produced if no fertilizer is used?

   _____

2. Write a mathematical model for the number of tomatoes produced using different amounts of fertilizer.

   _____

3. Using the model from Exercise 2, how many tomatoes do you predict will be produced if 8 tons of fertilizer are used per acre? 12 tons? 25 tons?

   _____

4. Do you think this model will work for 150 tons? Why or why not?

   _____

   _____

   _____

   _____

Holt Middle School Math   Course 2

LESSON	**Consumer Math**
12-1	*Homeowners Insurance*

Homeowner's insurance is purchased to protect the homeowner against loss or damage to their home. The annual premium paid depends on the amount of insurance coverage purchased for each type of damage or loss that could occur to the home (i.e., fire, flood, tornado, theft). Some insurance companies allow the policyholder to pay their premiums annually, semiannually, quarterly, or monthly. An extra charge is added for each of the last three payment plans.

For example, an insurance company charges an additional 2.5% of the basic rate for a policy that is paid semiannually. Find the total annual premiums for the following policies, $636.21 and $594.04, that are paid semiannually.

Input	Rule	Output
x	$x + 0.025x$	y
636.21	636.21 + 0.025(636.21)	652.12
594.04	594.04 + 0.025(594.04)	608.89

Use a table to show the input and output values for insurance premiums paid semiannually.

A $636.21 annual premium paid semiannually cost $652.12.
A $594.04 annual premium paid semiannually cost $608.89.

Solve.

1. An insurance company charges an additional 4.7% for a policy that is paid quarterly. Complete the table to find the total annual premiums for the following insurance policies if paid on a quarterly basis.

Input	Rule	Output
x	$x + 0.047x$	y
322.66		
417.45		
535.27		
587.11		

2. Find the rule to determine the total annual premium when an insurance company charges an additional 6.9% when the policy is paid on a monthly basis.

_____

3. Using the input values from Exercise 1, find the total annual premiums for these policies if they are paid on a monthly basis. Use your rule from Exercise 2.

_____

Holt Middle School Math   Course 2

Name _____ Date _____ Class _____

LESSON 12-2 Consumer Math
Public Transportation

Many commuters rely on public transportation to travel to and from work or to simply get around town. Public transportation includes taxis, buses, and trains. Consumers must budget for the use of these systems and set aside money on a weekly basis to make sure this expense is covered.

Rachel has budgeted $25.00 per week for traveling expenses. She will spend $3.50 round trip per day to get to and from work. How much money will she have left after five days to spend on additional travel around town? Find a pattern in the sequence.

n	Rule	y
1	25 − 1 • 3.50	21.50
2	25 − 2 • 3.50	18.00
3	25 − 3 • 3.50	14.50
4	25 − 4 • 3.50	11.00
5	25 − 5 • 3.50	7.50

If Rachel spends $3.50 per day for five days to get to and from work, she will have $7.50 left to complete any additional travel around town.

Solve.

1. Shannon purchased a $25.00 travel credit card to use at the train station. Each train trip costs $0.75. Write a sequence to find out how much credit she has left after taking 5 trips on the train.

2. Evan has 150,000 frequent travel miles for an airline. He earns 15,000 miles each time he travels from New York to Chicago. Write a sequence to determine how many frequent flyer miles he will have after making 7 trips.

3. Find a function that describes the sequence of taxi fares: $2.50, $5.00, $7.50, $10.00. Use the function to determine how much money will be spent after taking 11 trips in the taxi.

4. Janet has $150.00 per month to spend on transportation. It costs $4.50 each day to ride the bus. How much money will she have left after riding on the bus 20 times?

The city planner needs to decide how to **zone** 250 acres of undeveloped land in the northeast part of town. She will zone the land as either single-family residential housing or multifamily retirement housing.

A subcommittee presented the city planner with the following data. The planner will examine the trends in population growth for each age group and base her zoning decision on housing need.

Town Population From 1984 to 2002

Age	1984	1986	1988	1990	1992	1994	1996	1998	2000	2002
18–50 years	1,375	1,435	1,500	1,570	1,600	1,545	1,510	1,450	1,422	1,375
over 50 years	1,035	1,150	1,295	1,410	1,595	1,655	1,715	1,775	1,830	1,900

Using the data, the city planner created the following double bar graph.

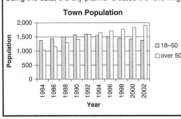

Use the information above for the following exercises.

1. Find the range of years that the population for the 18 to 50 age group increased.

   1984 to 1992

2. Find the range of years that the population for the over 50 age group increased.

   1984 to 2002

3. Given the current trend in population estimate the population of the over 50 age group in 2004.

   a little more than 2,000 people

4. Based on the data, how would you zone the property if you were the City Planner?

   multifamily retirement

2   Holt Middle School Math   Course 2

Emily must report commission earnings of her sales department for the month of May to the regional sales office. Commission is a percent of the dollar value of sales over a specified period of time. In her report, she must provide the range, mean, median and mode of commissions paid for the month.

Commission Report

Employee	Jan	Feb	Mar	Apr	May
Janice	$650	$772	$595	$697	$750
Fred	$772	$489	$683	$805	$695
Jose	$598	$637	$783	$492	$767
Nicki	$650	$689	$675	$650	$695
Charlie	$805	$945	$595	$737	$595

Emily made the following calculations for her report.

Range = $767 − $595 = $172   Subtract the smallest value from the greatest value.

Median = $695   Arrange the values in numerical order and find the middle value.

Mode = $695   Find the value that occurs most often.

Mean $= \dfrac{\$750 + \$695 + \$767 + \$695 + \$595}{5} = \$700.40$ Find the average.

Use the Commission Report table above for each exercise.

1. Find Jose's mean commission for the months January through May.

   $655.40

2. What is the range of commission for Charlie over the past five months?

   $945 − $595 = $350

3. How much less is the median commission for March than May?

   $20

4. How much more is the mode for January and February than the mode for May?

   $77

5. A bonus of $200 will go to any sales person who has a median commission greater than $695. Which employee(s) will get the bonus?

   Janice, Charlie

6. Which employee(s) has a mean commission for the months shown greater than the mean commission for the month of May?

   Charlie

3   Holt Middle School Math   Course 2

A line graph can be used to evaluate the performance of a company's **stock** over time. Individuals purchase stock as an **investment.** Stocks are sold by companies as a means of generating money. Typically, as performance increases, the return on investment increases. The line graph shows the performance of Tristate Restaurants over the past year. The investor can look at this graph to find trends in the stock performance and the relative health of the company.

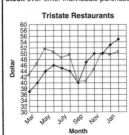

Use the line graph for each exercise.

1. During which month was there the biggest increase in stock price?

   October

2. Overall, how much has the stock risen from last March to this February?

   $18.00

3. Using the same graph above, plot the points in the table below to make a double line graph.

Home Living Stock Prices

Mar	Apr	May	Jun	Jul	Aug	Sep	Oct	Nov	Dec	Jan	Feb
42	46	51	50	48	49	40	40	44	50	49	50

4. In the first six months, which company appears to have performed better?

   Home Living

5. During which month was there a sharp decrease in the value of the stock for both companies?

   September

4   Holt Middle School Math   Course 2

An astronomer works with numbers so large in size that it is cumbersome not only to write these numbers, but also very confusing when trying to work with them. Astronomers believe that there are 100 quintillion stars in the universe. Written in standard form this number would look like 100,000,000,000,000,000,000. It is easier for an astronomer to use a "shorthand" approach to displaying this number by writing it in scientific notation as 1×10^{20}.

It has been estimated that the distance to the sun is 93 million miles. Written in **standard form,** this number is written as 93,000,000 miles. Astronomers write this number using **scientific notation.** In scientic notation the number is written as two factors, one being a number greater than or equal to 1 and less than 10, and the other being a power of 10. The exponent is equal to the number of places the decimal point is moved.

$93,000,000. = 9.3 \times 10^{7}$

In scientific notation the number is written as 9.3×10^{7}.

Complete.

1. The distance from Mercury to the sun is 35,990,000 miles. Write this number in scientific notation.

   3.599×10^{7}

2. The distance from Venus to the sun is 6.7239×10^{7} miles. Write this number in standard form.

   67,239,000

3. The distance from Mars to the sun is 1.4136×10^{8} miles. Write this number in standard form.

   141,360,000

4. The distance from Jupiter to the sun is 483,600,000 miles. Write this number in scientific notation.

   4.836×10^{8}

5. The distance from Saturn to the sun is 887,220,000 miles. If you write the number in scientific notation, what is the exponent on the factor of 10?

   8

6. The distance from Uranus to the sun is 1,783,700,000 miles. How many places do you have to move the decimal point to write the number in scientific notation?

   9 places

6   Holt Middle School Math   Course 2

Raphael works for Hamburg Industries as an **hourly** employee. An hourly employee is paid for each hour spent working on the job. This is called **straight pay.** Typically, hourly employees are paid additional wages for any hours worked over a normal 40-hour work week. This is called **overtime pay.**

Raphael worked 63 hours last week. What was his total pay if his straight pay is $7.50 per hour and overtime pay is $11.25 per hour?

($7.50 × 40) + $11.25(63 − 40) Write an expression.

$300 + $11.25(23)	Perform operations in parentheses first.
$300 + $258.75	Multiply.
$558.75	Add.

Raphael's total pay for last week was $558.75.

Solve.

1. Kaitlin worked 56 hours this week. What was her total pay for the week if her straight pay is $8.00 per hour and overtime pay is $12.00 per hour?

   $512.00

2. Randolph earns $6.50 per hour straight pay and $9.75 per hour overtime pay. If he works 61 hours in a week, what will be his total pay?

   $464.75

3. Gary is paid $17.00 straight pay and $25.50 overtime pay. If he made $884.00 for the week, how many hours did he work?

   48 hours

4. Sandra made $656.00 last week. She earns $8.00 per hour straight pay and $12.00 per hour overtime pay. How many overtime hours did she work?

   28 hours

5. Nicholas is paid $9.50 per hour straight pay and $14.25 per hour overtime pay. He made $1,144.75 for the past two weeks he worked. How many overtime hours did he work over the last two weeks?

   27 hours

6. Muriel earned $1573.44 for the month of June. If she makes $7.25 per hour straight pay and $10.88 per hour overtime pay, how many overtime hours did she work for the month? (*Hint:* 4 weeks in a month)

   38 hours

7 Holt Middle School Math Course 2

Darian earns **piece-work wages** at Starlink Corporation. Employees who are paid piece-work wages are paid a specified amount of money for each article or unit produced. Each article or unit produced is called a **piece** and the dollar amount received for each piece is called the **piece rate**. Piece-work wages can be expressed as:

$W = p \times r$ Where W represents the wages, p represents the number of pieces produced, and r represents the piece-rate paid.

If Darian produced 235 circuit boards in a week and earns $411.25, find his piece-work rate.

$W = p \times r$	Write the formula.
$411.25 = 235 \times r$	Substitute known values in the equation.
$\frac{411.25}{235} = r$	Divide each side by 235 and solve for r.
$1.75 = r$	

Darian makes a piece-work rate of $1.75.

Complete.

1. Diane is paid $1.35 for each unit produced. She earns $171.45 for the day. Write and solve an equation to find how many units she produced in a week.

   $171.45 = p × $1.35; 127 units

2. Joshua earns 3 times as much as Tim for producing the same transistors. If each produces 176 units, write an expression to find Joshua's piece-work rate.

   3r × 176

3. Mickey is paid $1.15 for each computer chip he produces. He worked five days last week. The first four days he produced 106 units, 97 units, 98 units and 102 units. His total wages for the week were $591.10. Write and solve an equation to find how many computer chips he made on the fifth day.

   $591.10 = (403 + p) × $1.15; 111 computer chips

4. Kitrina is a seamstress in a garment factory. In an 8-hour workday she assembled 12 blouses and 2 skirts. She is paid $15.30 for each blouse she makes. She is paid $20.00 for each skirt she makes. Write and solve an equation to determine Kitrina's hourly rate.

   8w = (12 × $15.30) + (2 × $20); approximately $27.95 per hour

8 Holt Middle School Math Course 2

Accountants often determine the **net income** or **net loss** for a corporation or sole proprietor for a certain period of time. This time period can be one month, 6 months, a year, or any other time period defined by the client. The formula used to determine net income (positive value) or loss (negative value) is:

Net Income or Loss = Revenue − Expenses

Revenue is the accounts represented by the sales of a product or service. **Expenses** are accounts that represent the cost of doing business.

Determine the net income or loss given the information in the table. The table is based on revenue and expenses for the past 6 months.

Hare Accessories

Revenue	$54,000
Rent	$724 per month
Salaries	$8,000
Supplies	$2,100

Net Income/Loss = Revenue − Expenses
= $54,000 − [6($724) + $8,000 + $2,100]
= $54,000 − [$4,344 + $8,000 + $2,100]
= $39,556

Since the result is positive, Hare Accessories shows a net income of $39,556 for the past 6 months.

Determine the net income or net loss.

1. Revenue = $16,000
   Supplier Expense = $4,000
   Salary Expense = $6,500

   Net Income of $5,500

2. Sales Revenue = $1,350
   Salaries Expense = $1,500
   Advertising Expense = $350

   Net Loss of $500

3. In 3 months, Mime Inc. has recorded a service revenue of $5,800, rental expense of $1,250 per month, salary expense of $3,000 and a sales revenue of $5,200. How much money have they earned or lost in 3 months?

   They have a net income of $4,250.

4. In 4 months, Data Inc. has recorded an insurance expense of $980 per month, service revenue of $4,800, and an advertising expense of $450 per month. How much money have they earned or lost in 4 months?

   They have a net loss of $920.

10 Holt Middle School Math Course 2

A **profit and loss statement** is a financial document that shows the annual overall profit or loss of a business. A profit and loss statement lists earnings for sales or services provided, the cost of goods or services provided, operating expenses such as wages paid, rent and advertising, and the total income or loss. Income items are positive numbers and expenses are negative numbers. By adding the income and expenses, the business owner can determine the overall profit or loss.

Last year a small business owner generated $230,000 in sales. He paid his employees $90,000 in wages, and spent $69,700 for rent, advertising and miscellaneous business expenses and supplies. Determine the overall profit or loss from the business.

$230,000 + (−$90,000) + (−$69,700)	Find the sum using negative numbers for expenses.
$230,000 − $90,000 − $69,700	Find the difference of the absolute values.
$70,300	The answer is positive.

The business made a $70,300 profit.

Solve.

1. Jerry made $4,000 mowing lawns over the summer. He spent $350 for a new lawn mower, $100 for advertising and $500 for gas. Did he make a profit or loss? How much was it?

   profit of $3,050

2. Chris started an arcade business last year. The total earnings for the year were $140,700. The equipment and supplies to start the business cost $83,000; wages to employees were $56,160; rent was $7,500; and advertising cost $3,550. Did he make a profit or loss? How much was it?

   loss of $9,510

3. Terry earned $31,250 for hanging wallpaper. He spent $625 for supplies and $1,275 for transportation costs. Did he make a profit or loss? How much was it?

   profit of $29,350

11 Holt Middle School Math Course 2

Consumer Math
Average Daily Change

A business owner must keep track of the average daily change of money coming into and out of the business. To determine the average daily change, the bank account must be monitored to keep track of the deposits and withdrawals made each day. When a business owner has an accurate picture of money flow, he will be confident that money will be available to keep the operations of the business running smoothly.

The table below shows a businesses bank account deposits and withdrawals over a 7-day period. What is the average daily change of funds in the account?

Day	Sun	Mon	Tues	Wed	Thurs	Fri	Sat
Amount ($)	627	−375	652	558	−295	−598	726

$627 + (−375) + 652 + 558 + (−295) + (−598) + 726$ Find the sum of the changes in money.

$\frac{1295}{7} = 185$ Divide by 7 to find the average for the week.

The average daily change in the account is $185.

Use the table for each exercise.

Cash Flow for Animators Inc.

	Sun	Mon	Tues	Wed	Thurs	Fri	Sat
Week 1	$ 636	$−323	$ 422	$ 617	$−227	$−420	$ 730
Week 2	$ 123	$−416	$ 524	$ 619	$−322	$ 762	$−121
Week 3	$ 413	$−351	$−125	$ 752	$ 430	$−328	$ 630
Week 4	$ 224	$−275	$ 565	$−431	$ 692	$−123	$ 783

1. What was the average daily change in the account for week 2?

   $167

2. What was the difference between the average daily change for week 1 and week 3?

   $2.00

3. What was the average daily change for all 4 weeks (28 days)?

   $195

   Holt Middle School Math   Course 2

CHAPTER 4

Career Math
Operations with Rational Numbers, continued

Ms. Tabor is a dietitian for the local middle school. To achieve a vegetable requirement, she determines that potato salad should be served for lunch on Wednesdays. She has a recipe for potato salad that makes 10 servings. She needs to convert the recipe in order to make enough potato salad to serve 200 students. Using the recipe below, find the amount of potatoes needed to make 200 servings.

Potato Salad (Serves 10)

$3\frac{1}{6}$ pound potatoes	$1\frac{3}{8}$ cups pickle relish
$1\frac{1}{4}$ pound onions	$\frac{1}{4}$ tablespoon paprika
$\frac{5}{6}$ pound celery	$\frac{1}{4}$ cup mustard
$\frac{2}{3}$ tablespoon pepper	$\frac{1}{3}$ tablespoon salt

To convert the recipe to serve 200 students, first divide the number of servings needed by the number of servings of the recipe: $200 \div 10 = 20$. Then, multiply the amount of the ingredient, potatoes, by a factor of 20.

$3\frac{1}{6} \times 20$ Multiply pounds of potatoes in the recipe by 20.

$3\frac{1}{6} \times 20 = \frac{19}{6} \times 20 = \frac{19}{6} \times \frac{\overset{10}{\cancel{20}}}{1} = \frac{190}{3} = 63\frac{1}{3}$

In order to serve 200 students, $63\frac{1}{3}$ lbs of potatoes will be needed.

Solve.

1. Using the recipe for potato salad shown above, how many pounds of onions will you need to make 200 servings?

   25 pounds

2. Using the recipe for potato salad shown above, how many cups of pickle relish will you need to make 50 servings?

   $6\frac{7}{8}$ **cups**

3. One serving of the cafeteria's tomato soup contains 200 mg of sodium (salt). The school's dietitian suggests that a serving should only have $\frac{2}{3}$ of this amount. How many milligrams of sodium should the soup contain?

   $133\frac{1}{3}$ **mg**

4. One serving of the cafeteria's chicken potpie contains 320 calories. The school's dietitian suggests that the football players eat $1\frac{2}{3}$ servings for lunch. How many calories are in $1\frac{2}{3}$ serving of potpie?

   $533\frac{1}{3}$ **calories**

   Holt Middle School Math   Course 2

Consumer Math
Budget Expenses

A **budget** is a spending and savings plan based on an estimate of income and expenses. While the main purpose of a budget is to help you live within your means, the budget process itself has many other benefits. It can help you save toward goals, identify spending patterns, and perhaps make changes in the way you spend your money. A budget should include fixed and variable expenses. **Fixed expenses** are costs such as car payments, and rent or mortgage payments that do not change each month. **Variable expenses** are costs such as food, utilities, phone bills, etc., that may change each month.

Category	Rent	Car	Phone	Food	Utilities	Total
Budgeted Amount	$500.00	$214.31				
Actual Expense Jan.	$500.00	$214.31	$42.55	$145.33	$176.33	
Actual Expense Feb.	$500.00	$214.31	$38.21	$119.56	$177.98	
Actual Expense Mar.	$500.00	$214.31	$39.87	$112.78	$181.24	

The spreadsheet above represents Maria Moeller's personal **budget.** How much should Maria budget for her utilities?

To determine the amount to budget for a variable expense, compute a multiple month average. The average amount of Maria's utilities can be found by adding the actual expenses for January, February and March, and dividing the result by the total number of months, 3.

$\frac{\$176.33 + \$177.98 + \$181.24}{3} = \$178.52$

Maria should budget $178.52 for her utilities.

Use the information above for each problem.

1. How much should Maria budget each month for food?

   $125.89

2. How much should Maria budget each month for phone expenses?

   $40.21

3. How much should Maria's total monthly budget be for all of her fixed and variable expenses?

   $1,058.93

4. Maria's monthly car payment is a fixed expense. How much will Maria have paid after one full year of payments?

   $2,571.72

   Holt Middle School Math   Course 2

Consumer Math
Purchase Order Forms

For record keeping purposes, many companies use **purchase order forms** when purchasing various quantities of items. A purchase order form shows the item number, a description, the quantity ordered, the unit price, the amount for each item, and the total amount to be purchased.

Purchase Order Form

Item	Description	Quantity	Unit Price	Amount
A3321	Ink Pens	12	$0.23	$2.76
A3556	Black Markers	4	$0.51	$2.04
C9987	Color Printer Cartridge	2	$21.33	$42.66
C7765	Computer Paper (Box)	4	$5.36	$21.44
D0012	Paper Clips (Box)	5	$0.83	$4.15
			Total Purchase	$73.05

Roberto is an administrative assistant for the local electric company. One of his responsibilities is to order office supply items using a purchase order form, as shown above. What is the total amount Roberto should enter for the ink pens?

Unit Price × Quantity = Total Amount per item

$0.23 × 12 = $2.76   Roberto should enter $2.76 in the purchase order for ink pens.

Enter this amount in the purchase order form.

Solve each problem and complete the purchase order form.

1. Find the amount Roberto should enter for the Black Markers.

   $2.04

2. Find the amount Roberto should enter for the Color Printer Cartridges.

   $42.66

3. If Computer Paper can be purchased at $5.36 per box, how many boxes did Roberto order for $21.44?

   4

4. Roberto ordered 5 boxes of paper clips for a total cost of $4.15. What is the unit price per box?

   $0.83

5. What is the Total Purchase amount for the purchase order?

   $73.05

   Holt Middle School Math   Course 2

---

51   Holt Middle School Math   Course 2

Proportional Reasoning, continued

In March 1989, 11.2 million gallons of oil spilt into Alaska's Prince William Sound as a result of an oil tanker accident. Nearly 10,000 square miles were affected by the spill, including a national forest, wildlife refuges, and game sanctuaries.

A 2,000 ml water sample taken from a contaminated lake contained 0.9 ml of oil by-products. What is amount of oil by-product in the 300,000-gallon lake?

$\frac{0.9 \text{ ml}}{2,000 \text{ ml}} = \frac{x \text{ gallons}}{300,000 \text{ gallons}}$ Write the proportion.

$2,000x = 0.9 \cdot 300,000$ Set the cross products equal.

$\frac{2,000x}{2,000} = \frac{270,000}{2,000}$ Divide each side by 2,000 to isolate the variable.

$x = 135$ gallons

There is about 135 gallons of oil by-product in the lake.

Write a proportion for each problem. Solve.

1. To clean up beaches affected by the oil spill, environmental scientists used fertilizer to promote growth of microscopic bacteria that eat the hydrocarbons in the oil. This process is known as **bioremediation.** If the scientists deposited 2,500 mg of bacteria for every 25 square yards, how much bacteria did they use for 1,000 square yards?

$\frac{2,500}{25} = \frac{x}{1,000}$; $x = 100,000$ mg

2. For every seabird carcass found by the oil clean up crew, scientist predicted 7 times more seabirds had probably died. If clean up crews found 35,000 dead seabirds, how many did the scientists record as dying?

$\frac{35,000}{1} = \frac{x}{7}$; $x = 245,000$ seabirds recorded dead

3. Reaching collection sites to obtain data was often difficult for the scientists because of the terrain. If a scientist had to climb a steep cliff he needed to insert a camming device into the cliff every 12 feet. This was to protect him in case of a fall. If a cliff was 119 feet high, how many camming devices did the scientist use? (Round up to the nearest whole number.)

$\frac{12}{1} = \frac{119}{x}$; $x = 10$ camming devices

18   **Holt Middle School Math   Course 2**

Unit Pricing

Wholesale clubs are very popular with today's consumer. The term **wholesale** means that the store is in the business of buying goods in quantity at discounted prices, usually direct from manufacturers or distributors, in order to sell them to the consumer. Typically, consumers can purchase the products they need at cheaper prices if they are willing to buy large quantities. The best way to determine the amount of savings is to calculate the **unit price** of the items purchased at the wholesale club and compare it to the retail unit price.

You purchase an 8-roll bundle of paper towels from a wholesale club. The cost for the bundle was $15.95. You could purchase 2 rolls of the same brand of paper towels at your local grocery store for $4.28. To determine which is the better value, you calculate the unit price for each purchase.

$\frac{\$15.95}{8 \text{ rolls}} = \$1.99$ per roll   wholesale unit price

$\frac{\$4.28}{2 \text{ rolls}} = \$2.14$ per roll   retail unit price

The paper towels at the wholesale club are a better value.

Solve.

1. Joel purchased a 60-oz box of his favorite cereal at a wholesale club for $12.59. Find the unit price of the cereal.

$0.21/oz

2. With a coupon, Joel could purchase 20 oz of the same cereal for $3.99 at the grocery store. Which is the better value?

retail = $0.20/oz; the retail store

3. Liz needs to purchase a set of 4 tires. The price at the wholesale club is $175, including installation. What is the unit price of the tires?

$43.75/tire

4. The tire store's price was $50 per tire including installation. How much did Liz save by buying 4 tires at the wholesale club?

$25.00

5. Marta buys a 32 oz. bottle of shampoo at the wholesale club for $11.96. Find the unit price of the shampoo.

$0.37/oz

6. At the salon, the same shampoo costs $6.95 for 12 oz. Which shampoo is the better value?

retail = $0.58/oz; wholesale

19   **Holt Middle School Math   Course 2**

Gas Mileage

When planning to purchase a new automobile, one factor to consider is the car's gas mileage. **Gas mileage,** listed as miles per gallon or mpg, is the number of miles the car runs for each gallon of gas. Automotive manufactures provide information on gas mileage for each model of automobile they produce. In fact, it is listed right on the sticker price of the car in big bold letters.

Suppose you want to buy a new car that averages 16 mpg on the highway. Because of your commute to work, you will be driving the car about 600 miles per week. Determine your cost per week to drive this car if the average price for gasoline is $1.59 per gallon.

Find the number of gallons you need to travel 600 miles.

$600 \text{ miles} \cdot \frac{1 \text{ gallon}}{16 \text{ miles}} = 37.5$ gallons

Multiply the number of gallons by the price of gasoline.

$37.5 \text{ gallons} \cdot \frac{\$1.59}{\text{gallon}} = \$59.63$

It will cost you about $60 per week to drive your car.

Solve.

1. Marco's drove his economy car, which gets 44 mpg on the highway, 396 miles to visit his family. He paid $1.29 per gallon of gasoline each time he needed gas. How much did he spend in gasoline?

$11.61

2. Hans wants to buy a new car that averages 18 mpg in the city. He plans to drive the car about 225 miles per week. How many gallons of gas per week will Hans use?

12.5 gallons

3. Gabby drives her car 300 miles per week. Each week she uses 20 gallons of gas. What kind of gas mileage does her car get?

15 mpg

4. If Gabby pays an average of $1.39 per gallon of gasoline, about how much per week does it cost to drive her car?

about $28

5. Which vehicle would be cheaper to take on a 350-mile round trip, your car that gets 12 mpg or a $60 rental car that gets 45 mpg? Gas is $1.43 per gallon.

The personal car is $29.42 cheaper.

20   **Holt Middle School Math   Course 2**

Percents, continued

Terrence is a human resource professional who specializes in compensation. Every year Terrence has to establish a salary increase procedure for the employees of the company. Typically, the company sets aside a percentage of its annual budget to allow for increases in the employees' salaries.

Terrence works for a manufacturing company with an annual operating budget of $1,000,000. This year he budgeted that he would need 10% of the annual operating budget for salary increases. How much money will Terrence have to allocate to salary increases?

$\$1,000,000 \cdot \frac{10}{100} = \$100,000$ Change 10% to a fraction. Multiply.

Terrence will have $100,000 to allocate for salary increases.

Usually as part of an annual review, an employee is given a **raise,** an increase in salary, as a percentage of his current salary. For example, an employee makes $30,000 per year and is given a 5% raise at his annual review. How much is his raise? How much is his new salary?

$\$30,000 \cdot \frac{5}{100} = \$1,500$ Change 5% to a fraction. Multiply.

The new salary equals: Salary + Raise = New Salary
                          $30,000 + $1,500 = $31,500

The employee received a raise of $1,500. His new salary is $31,500.

Solve.

1. A company with an annual operating budget of $2,000,000 set aside 15% for salary increases. What amount did they set aside for salary increases?

$300,000

2. Shauna is scheduled to receive her annual salary increase next month. Her current salary is $42,000 per year. Calculate the amount of her raise, and her new salary if she gets a 7% raise.

$2,940; $44,940

3. Molly earns $7.00 per hour at the paper mill. At her annual review she was told that she would receive a $0.35 per hour increase in pay. What percent increase did she receive?

5%

4. The operating budget for your company is $2,500,000 per year. The company budgeted $300,000 for salary increases. What percent is budgeted for salary increases?

12%

22   **Holt Middle School Math   Course 2**

---

52   **Holt Middle School Math   Course 2**

Consumer Math
6-4 Sales Tax

In the United States, most states have a general sales tax. State **sales tax** rates vary from state to state. **Sales taxes** are taxes on retail merchandise and are collected at the point of sale by the retailer. Taxation is used as a way to raise money to finance the government. Governments use tax revenues to pay soldiers and police, to build dams and roads, to operate schools and hospitals, to provide food to the poor and medical care for the elderly, as well as many other purposes. Without taxes to fund its activities, government could not exist. Taxation is the most important source of revenues for modern governments and typically accounts for 90 percent or more of their income.

Vinnie purchased a hat and a pair of socks. The sales tax on his purchase was $0.84. What percent sales tax was he charged?

Shirt	$15.50	Pants	$22.75
Hat	$7.50	Skirt	$24.50
Pair of Socks	$4.50	Boots	$29.00
Scarf	12.00	Shoes	$21.75

Find the cost of the purchase: $7.50 + 4.50 = $12.00.

$12x = 0.84$ Set up an equation.

$\frac{12x}{12} = \frac{0.84}{12}$ Divide both sides by 12 to isolate x.

$x = 0.07 = 7\%$ Divide. Convert the decimal to a percent.

Vinnie was charged a 7% sales tax rate.

Use the table above to answer each question.

1. Steve purchased a shirt, a pair of pants and a scarf. He is charged $52.76 for his purchase. What is the sales tax rate, to the nearest whole number?

   5%

2. Lisa bought a pair of boots and a pair of shoes. The sales tax on her purchase was $2.79. What percent sales tax did she pay?

   5.5%

3. Gloria bought 2 shirts and 3 pair of pants. The sales tax is 4.5%. How much did she pay in sales tax?

   $4.47

4. Sam purchased 2 scarves. He paid $1.20 in sales tax. What percent sales tax did he pay?

   5%

Holt Middle School Math   Course 2

Consumer Math
6-6 Simple Interest

When money is borrowed or invested, **interest** is charged or earned for the use of that money for a certain period of time. The amount of interest depends on the interest rate, the **principal,** or amount of money borrowed or invested, and the length of time of the loan or investment. This type of interest is referred to as **simple interest.**

The formula for finding simple interest is:
Interest = Principal • Rate • Time or $I = P \cdot R \cdot T$

Calculate the simple interest on a $100 loan borrowed for 2 years at a 10% interest rate. Then find the total amount of money paid back to the bank.

$I = P \cdot R \cdot T$ Write the formula.

$I = 100 \cdot 0.10 \cdot 2$ Substitute known values. Convert the percent to a decimal.

$I = \$20$ Multiply.

The simple interest on the loan is $20.

The total amount paid back to the bank is the principal plus interest.
$100 + $20 = $120.

You would pay the bank a total of $120 for borrowing $100 for 2 years.

Solve.

1. Marcy bought a washer from an appliance store for $625. Marcy financing the entire amount for 1 year at a 25% interest rate. How much interest will Marcy pay? Find the total amount she will pay for the washer.

   $156.25; $781.25

2. Haley needs to borrow $1,000 to help pay for her tuition. A bank offers a loan at a rate of 8% for 3 years. How much interest will she pay for this loan? How much will she pay in total for the money?

   $240; $1,240

3. Shawn invested $2,000 in a simple interest certificate of deposit, five years ago. The interest rate was 6% for 5 years. How much money did Shawn have at the end of the 5 years?

   $2,600

4. Barney loaned his nephew $5,500 to buy a used car. His nephew agreed to pay him back in 1 year. At the end of the year, the nephew had paid his uncle a total of $6,050. What interest rate did his uncle charge?

   10%

Holt Middle School Math   Course 2

Career Math
7 Plane Figures, continued

An architect has the freedom to design with his artistic intuition. For instance, when putting a roof on a building or a home he can create a different visual affect, depending on the angle. A 180° roofline is flat, where as a 60° roofline is very steep. The ridge is the uppermost, horizontal external angle formed by the intersection of two sloping roof planes. Typically, the more rooflines on a house or building, and the steeper the roof, the more costly it is to construct. An architect's design might be guided by cost, but it also needs to be aesthetically pleasing to the eye.

A ridge with a 30° angle is formed by two sloping roof planes of equal measure. What is the angle measure of each plane? What type of triangle is formed?

Use the fact that the sum of the angles in a triangle equal 180°.

$30 + x + x = 180$ Set up the equation.

$30 + 2x = 180$ Add like terms.

$2x = 150$ Subtract 30 from both sides.

$x = 75$ Divide each side by 2 to isolate x.

Each plane measures 75°. Since two sides have equal measures, the triangle formed is an isosceles triangle.

Solve.

1. The angle of a roof ridge is designed to be 60°. The slope of the roof planes is shown to be the same on both sides of the ridge. The architect forgot to write down the angle measures on the drawing. What are the two missing angles? What type of triangle is formed?

   60°, 60°; equilateral triangle

2. The angle of a roof ridge was designed to be 75°, but the customer wants the architect to change it to 90°. The architect insists that the structure needs to have the slope of the roof plane angles equal. What is the angle of each roof plane? What type of triangle is formed?

   45°, 45°; isosceles right triangle

3. The angles at the roofline of your aunt's house are 75° and 15°. What is the angle in the ridge? What type of triangle is formed?

   90°; right triangle

4. The angles at the roofline of a new house are 70° and 50°. What is the angle in the ridge? What type of triangle is formed?

   60°; scalene triangle

Holt Middle School Math   Course 2

Consumer Math
7-3 Toll Bridges

Bridges are strategically constructed for the purpose of permitting passage over water, land, and roads. Because of the expense of bridge construction and maintenance, some bridges charge a **toll,** a fee or payment, for the right or privilege to use it.

For the 2-lane bridge that connects the main land to the island in Ocean Park, a toll is charged. The table below shows the toll fees.

Type of Vehicle	Toll
Car	$0.50
SUV	$0.75
Camper or Trailer	$2.00
Semi Truck	$4.50

Use the chart and the picture of the bridge for each exercise.

1. About how much toll is collected in one week if an average of 200 cars cross the bridge per day?

   $700

2. Are the columns of the bridge parallel or perpendicular to the water below the bridge?

   perpendicular

3. Do the columns of the bridge appear to make a 45°, 60°, or 90° angle with the base of the bridge?

   90°

4. To bring supplies to the island, a truck comes to and from the island every day. How much does the truck pay in tolls for a 30-day period?

   $270

5. Are the 2-lanes on the bridge parallel or perpendicular to each other?

   parallel

6. What angle measure do the 2-lanes make with each other?

   180°

7. Some toll bridges, like the one shown, are over water. As a boat passes under the bridge, the drawbridge rises up so the boat can clear. If a flat drawbridge, parallel to the water, rises the center section to 70°, what angle does this section now make with the road?

   110°

8. The drawbridge in Exercise 7 charges a $15 toll to let a boat pass underneath it. On average, 75 boats per week pass under the bridge. How much money is collected in tolls per week? As a boat passes under the bridge, is it parallel or perpendicular to the road above it?

   $1,125; perpendicular

Holt Middle School Math   Course 2

Holt Middle School Math   Course 2

A circle graph can be used to show the estimated weekly operating budget for a local grocery store. A **budget** is a systematic plan for meeting expenses in a given time period.

The circle graph shows the estimated operating budget for a typical week.

Weekly Operating Budget

- Payroll 12%
- Utilities 3%
- Profit 1%
- State Sales Tax 5%
- Produce Suppliers 3%
- Meat Suppliers 20%
- Grocery Suppliers 56%

Approximately 3% of the weekly income must be budgeted for utilities, such as electric, gas, and water. What is the central angle measure of this sector on the circle graph?

The angular measure of a circle is 360°. Since the sector for utilities is 3% of the graph, then the central angle is 3% of the circle's angular measure.

3% of 360° = 0.03 × 360° = 10.8°

The central angle measure of the utility sector is 10.8°.

Use the circle graph above for each exercise.

1. What accounts for the largest weekly expense of the grocery store?

   grocery suppliers

2. What is the central angle measure of the sector from Exercise 1?

   201.6°

3. Which sector of the graph is a little less than 90°?

   meat suppliers

4. What is the actual central angle measure of the sector from Exercise 3?

   72°

5. How much of the budget is designated for payroll expense?

   12%

6. What central angle measure is used to show the amount budgeted for payroll expense?

   43.2°

Holt Middle School Math Course 2

A construction manager needs to fence in a job site to prevent unauthorized entry into the hardhat or construction area. The building being constructed measures 1,600 feet by 2,880 feet. The manager needs to leave 135 feet on each side of the building for adequate space to work.

To determine how much fence he needs, find the perimeter of the construction site.

2(1,600 + 135 + 135) • 2(2,880 + 135 + 135) = 10,040 ft

The construction manager needs to order 10,040 feet of fence.

Solve.

1. A construction site measures 600 yards on all 4 sides. Find the perimeter of the site.

   2,400 yards

2. What is the perimeter of a construction site that measures 185 ft by 227 ft?

   824 feet

3. A trucking company is constructing a facility close to the highway. The facility will be in the shape of a polygon with 4 unequal sides. The sides will measure $\frac{1}{2}$ mile, $\frac{2}{5}$ mile, $\frac{1}{4}$ mile and $\frac{1}{5}$ mile. Find the perimeter of the facility.

   $1\frac{7}{20}$ mile

4. Construction on a new aquatic center is scheduled to begin next month. The shape of the construction site is a regular pentagon, with each side measuring 500 feet. Find the perimeter of the site.

   2,500 feet

5. Before a building can be constructed, the construction manager schedules the footers of the building to be poured. The base of the building measures 500 m x 435 m. Find the area of the base of the building.

   217,500 m²

6. A circular fountain is being renovated at Southsea Park. The fountain has a 24-ft diameter. The construction manager fences in the area around the fountain to prevent unauthorized entry into the site. The diameter of the fenced area is 40 ft. Find the area of the construction site.

   1,256 ft²

Holt Middle School Math Course 2

In Alex's community, water is billed according to the number of monthly gallons of water used.

Water Usage Chart

Gallons Used	Cost
first 2,000 gallons	$12.50
remaining gallons	$4.75 per 1,000 gallons

Alex's family uses 4,000 quarts of water every month washing dishes. What is the cost of this water consumption?

4,000 quarts • $\frac{1 \text{ gallon}}{4 \text{ quarts}}$ = 1,000 gallons   There are 4 quarts in 1 gallon.

The water usage cost Alex's family $12.50

Solve. Use the information above.

1. In one month Eric used 1,200 gallons of water washing his cars and 2,000 quarts of water running his faucets. How many total gallons of water did Eric use?

   1,700 gallons

2. In one month Rick used 3,000 gallons of water watering his yard and 3,000 quarts of water running his washing machine. How many total gallons of water did Rick use?

   3,750 gallons

3. Determine Eric's water usage bill from Exercise 1.

   $12.50

4. Determine Rick's water usage bill from Exercise 2.

   $20.81

5. A town gives a once a year pool credit of 39,400 quarts. A pool credit allows people to fill their pool and not pay charges on the water needed to fill it. Chuck used 18,560 gallons of water in May plus an additional 11,400 gallons to fill his pool.

   a. How many gallons of water can Chuck claim as a pool credit?

   9,850 gallons

   b. How many gallons of water will Chuck be billed for the month of May? (Deduct the pool credit.) What is the amount of his water bill?

   20,110 gallons; $98.52

Holt Middle School Math Course 2

When working on a home improvement project, it is best to get a good value on the materials you need to purchase. The table lists the price of floor tiles.

Type Tile	Single Price	Box Price
Vinyl (12-inch square)	$1.45	$35.00 per box of 30
Ceramic (6-inch square)	$0.75	$18.00 per box of 28
Ceramic (12-inch square)	$2.50	$35.00 per box of 15

The floor you need to cover is 9 ft by 9 ft. If you use the 6-inch ceramic tiles, should you buy tiles by the box or a combination of each?

Find the area of the floor.
9 feet × 9 feet = 81 square feet

Find the number of tiles needed. You will need 4 tiles for each square foot.
81 square feet × 4 = 324 tiles

Find the number of boxes of tiles.
Number of boxes = $\frac{324}{28}$ = 11.6 boxes. Round to 12 full boxes.

Find the cost if buying only full boxes of tiles.
12 boxes × $18 = $216

Find the cost if buying a combination of each.
(11 boxes × $18) + (16 tiles × $0.75) = $210

Buying a combination of boxes and individual tiles is the better buy.

Use the information above for each excercise.

1. If you decided to install the 12-inch ceramic tiles, how many boxes and individual tiles would you need?

   5 boxes and 6 individuals

2. What is the cost for the tiles in Exercise 1?

   $190

3. You found the same 12-inch ceramic tile for $25 per box at a discount store. You can only purchase full boxes. What is the tile cost?

   $150

4. The vinyl tile is not as decorative but it is easier to install. What is the best buy, boxes of tiles or individual tiles for the floor? What is the cost?

   3 full boxes; $105

Holt Middle School Math Course 2

---

54 **Holt Middle School Math Course 2**

Geometry: Volume and Surface Area, continued

Bill is the new owner of an oceanside restaurant. He hopes 50% of his total profits can be realized from beverage sales. His basic glassware is shaped like a cylinder and comes in two sizes. Bill wants to know how much each glass holds, and the beverage cost to fill each glass before setting his prices. The smaller glass has a 1.5-inch radius and is 6.5 inches tall. The larger glass has a 2.75-inch radius and is 8 inches tall. Bill's average beverage cost is $0.02 per cubic inch. What is the cost to fill each sized glass?

Volume of a cylinder $= \pi r^2 h$
Volume of smaller glass $= 3.14 \times 1.5^2 \times 6.5 \approx 46$ in^3
Volume of larger glass $= 3.14 \times 2.75^2 \times 8 \approx 190$ in^3

Total Beverage Cost $=$ Volume $\times$ Cost per cubic inch
Cost of smaller glass $= 46$ in$^3 \times \$0.02 = \$0.92$
Cost of larger glass $= 190$ in$^3 \times \$0.02 = \$3.80$

Solve.

1. Bill wants to offer another beverage size midway between his current glass sizes described above. He can choose from one of these options:
   A) radius 1.75 in., height 6.75 in.
   B) radius 2 in., height 7 in.
   C) radius 2.25 in., height 7.25 in.
   Which glass size should Bill purchase? What will it cost to fill the glass?

   Option C, cost = $2.30

2. At the carryout window on the oceanside of the restaurant, Bill sells spherically shaped popcorn balls in two sizes. One ball is 4 inches in diameter the other ball size is 5 inches in diameter. Bill's cost for the popcorn is $0.015 per cubic inch popped. What is the volume, to the nearest cubic inch, of each popcorn ball? What is Bill's cost for each?

   33 in^3, 65 in^3; $0.50, $0.98

3. For July 4th, Bill wants to put special lettering on his largest cylindrical plastic cups. The cups have a 2-inch radius and are 7 inches tall. The cost, per hundred cups, to apply the lettering is $10 for lateral surface areas of 50 in^2 to 75 in^2, and $15 for 76 in^2 to 100 in^2. What will be Bill's cost for 100 cups?

   $15 per 100 (88 in^2)

4. Bill wants to build a large aquarium in the entryway to his restaurant. The fish store owner next door will maintain the aquarium for $10 per cubic foot per month. If the aquarium is a rectangular prism 6 feet long, 1.5 feet wide, and 3 feet high, what will be Bill's monthly maintenance bill?

   $270

Shopping for Supplies

Decorative ceramic globes are currently a popular item. Spherical globes are painted with special paint and then covered with a decorative glaze. The cost to make the globes depends on the size of the globe and amount of paint needed to cover its surface.

Shari wants to make ten decorative ceramic globes to sell at a market. She needs to determine how much paint she will need to paint two coats of paint on each of ten 4-inch diameter globes. The paint comes in quart containers that cover 100 square feet.

Find the surface area of a 4-inch globe: $S = 4\pi r^2 = 4 \times 3.14 \times 2^2 = 50.24$ in^2
Find the surface area for 10 globes: 10×50.24 in$^2 = 502.4$ in^2
Calculate amount of paint, two coats per globe: $502.4 \times 2 = 1,004.8$ in^2

A quart of paint covers 100 ft^2. Convert this to square inches.

$$100 \text{ ft}^2 \times \frac{144 \text{ in}^2}{1 \text{ ft}^2} = 14,400 \text{ in}^2$$

The area for 10 globes is 1,004.8 in^2, so one quart of paint is needed.

Solve. Use the information given above if necessary.

1. Jamal wants to make as many 5-inch diameter globes, with two coats of paint per globe, as possible. How many globes can be painted from one quart of paint?

   91 globes

2. The specialty paint for ceramic globes costs $12 per quart. With two coats of paint for each globe, what is the per globe cost to paint each of the 5-inch globes from Exercise 1?

   $0.13 per globe

3. Alyce is making one hundred 5-inch globes. She plans to use a paint that requires only one coat but costs $20 per quart. Which paint is the most economical, the $20 or the $12 per quart?

   $20 per quart

4. Another popular craft project is painting wooden boxes with lids. Find the surface area of a wooden box that measures 12 in. × 10 in. × 6 in.

   504 in^2

5. How many quarts of paint are needed to paint ten boxes in Exercise 4, inside and out, with two coats?

   2 quarts

6. Assume that the paint costs $12 per quart. Calculate the cost per box if Billy is painting 10 boxes.

   $2.40 per box

Packaging

Sweet Things Candy and Nut Shoppe carry a variety of specialty candies and nuts. They package their product in both glass jars and decorative boxes. Pricing is based on the amount the container will hold of a particular product.

The best selling package of nuts is a 3 in. × 4 in. × 2 in. box that holds 6-oz of special blended mixed nuts. The owner recently decided to package the nuts in a box similar to the 6-oz box, but larger by a factor of 2. How many ounces of nuts will this new box hold?

New weight $=$ old weight • (factor)^3
New weight $= 6$ oz • 2^3
New weight $= 48$ oz

The new box will hold 48 oz of nuts.

Solve.

1. The best selling box of candy at Sweet Things holds 10 ounces of candy. How many ounces of candy would a similar box hold if it were increased by a factor of 1.5?

   33.75 oz

2. If the wholesale cost of nuts for the 3 in. × 4 in. × 2 in. box is $0.75. How much will it cost to fill a 48 oz box with the same type of nuts?

   $6.00

3. The wholesale cost of a fancy nut mixture is $2 per pound. How many 3 in. × 4 in. × 2 in. boxes can be completely filled with 10 pounds of this mix?

   26 boxes

4. The smallest cylindrical jar currently used to package candy has a $2\frac{1}{2}$ in. diameter and is 5 in. high. What is the volume of the next size jar if it is larger than the smaller jar by a factor of $1\frac{1}{2}$?

   82.79 cubic inches

5. Gulf Coast Graphics has been hired to design a label for the $2\frac{1}{2}$ in. × 5 in. cylindrical jar. If the label is to come within 1 in. of the top of the jar, what is the surface area of the label?

   31.4 in^2

6. How may full labels from Exercise 5 will Gulf Coast Graphics be able to get out of $8\frac{1}{2}$ in. × 14 in. paper stock?

   3 labels

Probability, continued

Food Service Managers have many responsibilities from scheduling employees, to determining daily menu specials.

Gisha received a shipment of fresh flounder (F) and salmon (S) from her seafood supplier, and fresh green beans (G), snow peas (P), and asparagus (A) from her vegetable supplier. Given these items, how many combinations of entrées can she make so that each dish is served with a fish and vegetable?

FG FP FA   List all of the entrées that contain flounder (F).
SG SP SA   List all of the entrées that contain salmon (S).
There are 6 possible combinations of entrées.

Solve.

1. The restaurant that Henry manages offers a salad with every entrée. The customer can choose between a spinach salad or a chef salad and five different salad dressings. How many possible salad choices are there?

   10

2. Dale likes to put vases of fresh flowers on each restaurant table. If each vase contains any of 5 different types of flowers, how many combinations of arrangements are possible?

   10

3. Ralph needs to call his fish, meat, vegetable, and linen suppliers today. What is the probability that he calls his vegetable supplier first?

   25%

4. Mindy is expecting 4 waiters to arrive at the restaurant between noon and 1:00 P.M. In how many different orders might the waiters arrive?

   24

5. For the past three weeks, Toni has been recording the sale of meatloaf. His records show that he sold more than 4 of these entrees 7 out of 21 days. What is the probability that he will sell more than 4 of these entrées on the 22nd day?

   $\frac{1}{3}$

6. Greta found that on 20 out of the past 30 days the blackened swordfish was ordered at least 10 times per day. What is the probability that at least 10 customers will order it on the 31st day? Is this a big selling item?

   $\frac{2}{3}$, yes

Consumer Math
10-1 Home Warranties

Many people who buy a home often purchase a **home warranty**. These warranty contracts remove the worry associated with the probability of something vital within the home breaking or failing during the first year the home is owned.

Gene and Janice are purchasing a 15-year old home. They can buy a home warranty for $325.00. They know that the average repair cost for home systems is $345 and the probability of a system breaking or failing is 33%. Find the probable annual cost of repairs to determine if they should purchase the warranty.

$345 × 0.33 = $113.85   Multiply the average repair cost by the probability.

$113.85 < $325.00   It is probable that Gene and Janice would save $211.15 if they do not buy the home warranty.

Use the table for each exercise.

Service	Average Replacement Cost	Probability of Occurrence
Central Heating/Cooling	$1,850.00	25%
Hot Water Tank	$225.00	30%
Dishwasher	$375.00	60%
Oven/Range	$995.00	40%

1. A home warranty costs $375.00. The new homeowner is worried about having to replace the furnace based on the results of the home inspection. Using the figures above, should the consumer purchase the warranty? Explain.

   Yes, the home owner could save $87.50 with the warranty.

2. The table above represents figures for homes that are older than 10 years. With newer homes, the probability of replacement drops. For example, the probability of an oven/range needing replacement decreases to 10%. Would it be favorable to purchase a $375 home warranty for a newer home? Explain.

   No, $99.50 is less than $375.

3. The new homeowner knows that the heating/cooling system and oven/range have been recently replaced. Would it still be wise to purchase a $375 home warranty?

   No, the probable annual cost of replacement for the dishwasher and hot water tank is only $292.50

Consumer Math
10-6 Grocery Budget

Many families who are on a strict household budget must carefully plan meals and shop wisely. To stay within a grocery budget and purchase as many food items as possible, the conscientious shopper may search for sales, buy store brands, or clip coupons. Others may attempt to buy in bulk from wholesale clubs and divide the merchandise into required serving sizes.

Mandy purchased chicken (C), steak (S), noodles (N), potatoes (P), green beans (G) and broccoli (B). How many different combinations of meals can she make if she serves a meat, a starch (noodles or potatoes), and a vegetable with each meal?

CNG, CNB, CPG, CNB   List all of the meals that begin with chicken.

SNG, SNB, SPG, SNB   List all of the meals that begin with steak.

There is a total of 8 combinations of meals that Mandy can make.

Solve.

1. Mary purchased several cuts of beef (B) when the grocery store was having a big sale. She also bought sweet potatoes (P), squash (S), rice (R), and carrots (C). If she prepares the beef with 2 side dishes, how many combinations of meals can she make?

   6 possible combinations

2. Rachel bought some "snack" items to put in her children's lunch bags. She bought carrot sticks (C), yogurt (Y), raisins (R), apples (A), and grapes (G). She will include 2 different snacks with each lunch. How many different combinations can she make with what she purchased?

   10 possible combinations

3. Pasta is a big hit in the Salvi household. Mrs. Salvi tries to be creative by adding different items to the pasta. This week she bought tomatoes (T), chicken (C), broccoli (B), and garlic (G). How many combinations can she make by combining the pasta with one other ingredient? Three ingredients?

   4 combinations; 4 combinations

4. When summer fruits are on sale, Greta likes to make fruit salad. She can choose from watermelon, cantaloupe, strawberries, peaches, kiwi, berries, and honeydew. If she combines 2 of these fruits with watermelon, how many combinations of fruit salad can she make?

   15 combinations

Career Math
11 Multistep Equations and Inequalities, continued

A market research analyst collects data to determine consumer preference, the sales of particular products, and public attitude. After the data is collected, the analyst evaluates it and interprets it to look for trends and then make recommendations.

A market research analyst is hired to help a political leader determine public support on an important issue. After designing a survey and collecting data from 1,300 people, the analyst found that twice as many women than men support the issue. If 600 people support the issue, how many are women and how many are men?

Let x = the number of men. So $2x$ = the number of women.

$x + 2x = 600$	Write an algebraic equation.
$3x = 600$	Add like terms.
$\frac{3x}{3} = \frac{600}{3}$	Solve for x.
$x = 200$	200 men support the issue.
$2x = 400$	400 women support the issue.

Solve.

1. A market research analyst was hired to determine which flavor of yogurt people in a certain area preferred. The analyst collected data from 2,000 people and found that people preferred Brand A three times as much than Brand B. How many people preferred Brand A? Brand B?

   Brand A = 1,500; Brand B = 500

2. Data was collected to investigate the sales of a particular type of snow ski. Sales over 3 years totaled $637,000. Sales were 4 times as much in the first year than the third year and twice as much in the second year from the third year. What were the total sales for each year?

   $364,000; $182,000; $91,000

3. A market research analyst is trying to determine if a franchise should be opened in a particular area. He found that four times as many people stated they would shop at the store than those who would not. If 1,500 people were surveyed, how many people said they would shop at the store?

   1,200 people

4. A market research analyst found that in a recent presidential election, 10% of the votes came from the West Coast, 25% from the Northeast, 20% from the Midwest, and 9 million votes came from the South. What was the total number of votes? How many votes came from the Midwest?

   20 million; 4 million

Consumer Math
11-1 What's a Dollar Worth?

Jordan wants to know how much a dollar today will be worth a year from now. In other words, she wants to know the **present value** of the dollar. The value of a dollar is affected by the **interest rate.** As interest rates rise, the present value of future dollars will fall, and when interest rates drop, the present value of the dollar held in the future will increase.

How much will $100 today be worth in terms of dollars you will have one year from now if the interest rate is 7% (0.07)?

The present value of a dollar is calculated as follows:

$F = \frac{1}{1+r}(T)$ Where r = interest rate, F = future dollars, and T = todays dollars.

$F = \frac{1}{1 + 0.07}(100)$ Substitute 0.07 for r, and 100 for T.

$F = 0.93 × 100$

$F = 93.00

So, $100 now will only be worth $93 in one year.

Solve.

1. If the interest rate is 5% (0.05), how much will $1,000 paid to you today be worth a year from now?

   $952.38

2. If the interest rate is 8% (0.08), what is the present value of $2,500 paid to you a year from now?

   $2,314.81

3. What is the future value of $25 paid to you today if the interest rate is 12% (0.12)?

   $22.32

4. What is the future value of $25 paid to you today if the interest rate is 3% (0.03)?

   $24.27

5. If the interest rate is 6% (0.06), how much will $45,000 be worth one year from now?

   $42,452.83

6. If interest rates drop to 2%, will $45,000 be worth more or less than when the interest rate is 6%?

   more

Consumer Math

11-2 What Do You Owe?

Almost all business owners require legal services to review and prepare documents, transactions, and various other legal matters. Lawyers usually charge businesses a base fee plus an hourly rate based on a **minimum billing time.** This means that if a legal service, such as a phone call made on your behalf, lasts for 2 minutes and your minimum billing time is $\frac{1}{10}$ hour (six minutes), you will be charged $\frac{1}{10}$ of the lawyer's hourly rate.

To determine the actual cost of legal expenses you need to know the minimum billable time and the lawyer's hourly rate. Find the amount a client owes for a meeting with his lawyer based on a base fee of $40, plus an additional hourly rate of $150, billed on a quarter-hour (15 minutes) basis.

Service	Base Fee	Minimum Billing Time	Hourly Rate	Actual Time Spent	Amount Due
Client Meeting	$40	$\frac{1}{4}$ hour	$150 per hour	38 minutes	?

Since the minimum billing time is every quarter of an hour, round up the actual time entry to the next 15-minute increment, 45 minutes. Multiply the total billable time, in hours, by the hourly rate and then add it to the base fee to determine the total amount of the bill.

$\left(\frac{45}{60} \cdot 150\right) + 40 = 152.50$ Change minutes to hours.

So, the client owes $152.50 for legal services.

Complete the table.

	Service	Base Fee	Minimum Billing Time	Hourly Rate	Actual Time Spent	Amount Due
1.	Letter writing	$35	$\frac{1}{4}$ hour	$100 per hour	22 minutes	$85.00
2.	Court appearance	$75	$\frac{1}{4}$ hour	$150 per hour	54 minutes	$225.00
3.	Meeting with prosecutor	$60	$\frac{1}{10}$ hour	$90 per hour	40 minutes	$123.00
4.	Meeting notes	$50	$\frac{1}{10}$ hour	$90 per hour	16 minutes	$77.00

44   Holt Middle School Math   Course 2

Career Math

12 Graphs and Functions, continued

A statistician is responsible for analyzing and interpreting data in many situations. Statisticians must use a variety of statistical equations and functions to help them to predict future events. Statisticians study the functional relationship between cause and effect. The effect that certain inputs have on a measured output is modeled using mathematical formulas.

For example, a statistician working in the government's agricultural department may want to find out how to best improve tomato farmers' yields. Experimental data from a leading agricultural university found the following data from using different amounts of fertilizer on a popular tomato plant.

Experimental Results

Tons of fertilizer used per acre, t	0	1	5	7	9	10	15	20
Number of tomatoes produced per acre, y	1,500	1,600	2,000	2,200	2,400	2,500	3,000	3,500

Use the table above to solve.

1. How many tomatoes are produced if no fertilizer is used?

   1,500

2. Write a mathematical model for the number of tomatoes produced using different amounts of fertilizer.

   $1,500 + 100t = y$

3. Using the model from Exercise 2, how many tomatoes do you predict will be produced if 8 tons of fertilizer are used per acre? 12 tons? 25 tons?

   2,300; 2,700; 4,000

4. Do you think this model will work for 150 tons? Why or why not?

   Probably not, because at some point additional amounts of fertilizer will not yield more tomatoes. In fact, it may cause *less* to be produced due to over-fertilization. At this point the linear mathematical model no longer applies.

46   Holt Middle School Math   Course 2

Consumer Math

12-1 Homeowners Insurance

Homeowner's insurance is purchased to protect the homeowner against loss or damage to their home. The annual premium paid depends on the amount of insurance coverage purchased for each type of damage or loss that could occur to the home (i.e., fire, flood, tornado, theft). Some insurance companies allow the policyholder to pay their premiums annually, semiannually, quarterly, or monthly. An extra charge is added for each of the last three payment plans.

For example, an insurance company charges an additional 2.5% of the basic rate for a policy that is paid semiannually. Find the total annual premiums for the following policies, $636.21 and $594.04, that are paid semiannually.

Input	Rule	Output
x	x + 0.025x	y
636.21	636.21 + 0.025(636.21)	652.12
594.04	594.04 + 0.025(594.04)	608.89

Use a table to show the input and output values for insurance premiums paid semiannually.

A $636.21 annual premium paid semiannually cost $652.12.
A $594.04 annual premium paid semiannually cost $608.89.

Solve.

1. An insurance company charges an additional 4.7% for a policy that is paid quarterly. Complete the table to find the total annual premiums for the following insurance policies if paid on a quarterly basis.

Input	Rule	Output
x	x + 0.047x	y
322.66	322.66 + 0.047(322.66)	$337.83
417.45	417.45 + 0.047(417.45)	$437.07
535.27	535.27 + 0.047(535.27)	$560.43
587.11	587.11 + 0.047(587.11)	$614.70

2. Find the rule to determine the total annual premium when an insurance company charges an additional 6.9% when the policy is paid on a monthly basis.

   $x + 0.069x$

3. Using the input values from Exercise 1, find the total annual premiums for these policies if they are paid on a monthly basis. Use your rule from Exercise 2.

   $344.92; $446.25; $572.20; $627.62

47   Holt Middle School Math   Course 2

Consumer Math

12-2 Public Transportation

Many commuters rely on public transportation to travel to and from work or to simply get around town. Public transportation includes taxis, buses, and trains. Consumers must budget for the use of these systems and set aside money on a weekly basis to make sure this expense is covered.

Rachel has budgeted $25.00 per week for traveling expenses. She will spend $3.50 round trip per day to get to and from work. How much money will she have left after five days to spend on additional travel around town? Find a pattern in the sequence.

n	Rule	y
1	25 − 1 • 3.50	21.50
2	25 − 2 • 3.50	18.00
3	25 − 3 • 3.50	14.50
4	25 − 4 • 3.50	11.00
5	25 − 5 • 3.50	7.50

If Rachel spends $3.50 per day for five days to get to and from work, she will have $7.50 left to complete any additional travel around town.

Solve.

1. Shannon purchased a $25.00 travel credit card to use at the train station. Each train trip costs $0.75. Write a sequence to find out how much credit she has left after taking 5 trips on the train.

   $25 − 0.75t; $24.25, $23.50, $22.75, $22.00, $21.25; She has $21.25 left.

2. Evan has 150,000 frequent travel miles for an airline. He earns 15,000 miles each time he travels from New York to Chicago. Write a sequence to determine how many frequent flyer miles he will have after making 7 trips.

   $150,000 + 15,000t$; He will have 255,000 miles.

3. Find a function that describes the sequence of taxi fares: $2.50, $5.00, $7.50, $10.00. Use the function to determine how much money will be spent after taking 11 trips in the taxi.

   Rule: multiply n by $2.50; $27.50

4. Janet has $150.00 per month to spend on transportation. It costs $4.50 each day to ride the bus. How much money will she have left after riding on the bus 20 times?

   $60.00

48   Holt Middle School Math   Course 2

---

57   Holt Middle School Math   Course 2

Antique-Style
DUCK DECOYS

Antique-Style
DUCK DECOYS

by Tom Matus

Fox
Chapel Publishing

1970 Broad Street • East Petersburg, PA 17520
www.FoxChapelPublishing.com

ISBN 978–1–56523–298–3

Publisher's Cataloging-in-Publication Data

Matus, Tom, 1962-

    Antique-style duck decoys / by Tom Matus. -- East Petersburg, PA :
Fox Chapel Publishing, c2006.

       p. ; cm.

      ISBN 978-1-56523-298-3

      Includes bibiliographical references.

      1. Decoys (Hunting)--Painting. 2. Wildlife wood-carving--
Technique. 3. Wood-carving--Technique. 4. Birds in art. I. Title.

TT199.75 .M38 2006
745.593/6--dc22   0604

To learn more about the other great books from
Fox Chapel Publishing, or to find a retailer near you,
call toll-free 1-800-457-9112 or visit us at *www.FoxChapelPublishing.com*.

Note to Authors: We are always looking for talented
authors to write new books in our area of woodworking, design,
and related crafts. Please send a brief letter describing your idea to
Peg Couch, Acquisition Editor, 1970 Broad Street, East Petersburg, PA 17520.

Printed in China
10 9 8 7 6 5 4 3 2

Alan Giagnocavo
Publisher

Peg Couch
Acquisition Editor

Gretchen Bacon
Editor

Troy Thorne
Design and Layout

Tom Matus
Sarah Freitas
Interior Photography

Greg Heisey
Cover & Gallery Photography

Acknowledgments

I would like to extend my sincere thanks to those who have attended my seminars in the past and who visit the website *www.decoycarvingforum.com* daily. You have provided the encouragement and enthusiasm to make a book like this become reality. Your suggestions and recommendations have been taken to heart, and you're the reason this book came together.

I would like to thank Steve Skees for impressing upon me "your own vision," "what you see in a bird," "how it feels," and "how it reflects time passed." You have provided more help than you know with just long talks of encouragement and support. You provided no details but spurred my curiosity beyond my ability. You're a true friend in believing in my talents. *Thank you.*

Ky Kraus—your passion for collecting decoys was evident when I first met you at a show in Ohio. Your enthusiasm for waterfowling is unmatched! Thank you for all of the help, guidance, and information you have provided over the years. I cannot thank you enough for your support. You're a true friend!

Sincere thanks to George Strunk. I never really appreciated the Delaware-River-style decoy until I actually slowed down and witnessed the fine detail that is required to make a decoy as fine as the ones you make. Your longevity and tenacity within this profession is a testament to your fine product. Thanks for the long phone calls talking duck! You have helped to provide that "light at the end of the tunnel."

Jon Groninger—when I need a laugh or a joke to pull me from a dull day, you provide that. That's why you're the idea man! Thanks for all of your help.

Chad Hauser, my left-hand man in a predominantly right-hand world! Thanks for your technical support on everything else I would ever need to know—you have the answers!

To my dad, Tony—you're with me on the marsh and on the water, providing that constant vigil.

I am most grateful for the loving support and guidance that my wife, Deborah, has provided while I was writing this book. Through your remarkable eye, you have helped guide and shape my carving career to where it is today. Please continue to provide that guiding light, for it is an inspiration and motivator for me. You have made this all possible, and I cannot thank you enough.

Contents

GETTING STARTED   CARVING THE DECOY   AGING THE WOOD   PAINTING   ANTIQUING

About the Author

Tom Matus

From his first entry in a decoy carving competition at the U.S. National Decoy Show in Amityville, New York, Tom Matus has proven himself as a premiere decoy carver. In the mid-1980s to the present, he has won more than 125 Best of Show ribbons and has garnered a number of awards and accolades, including five-time U.S. National Decoy Show Winner in Shore Birds, 2000 Ward Foundation World Champion, 2001 Nevada Carver of the Year, 2001 and 2003 California Ducks Unlimited Carver of the Year, and 2002 and 2004 International Wildfowl Carvers Association National Champion.

Tom was a featured artist for the DIY Network's *Woodsculpting* series with his own episode on how to carve a drake mallard decoy. He has also been featured in *Wildfowl Carving* magazine and *Wood Carving Illustrated. Duck Decoys*, Tom's first book, was published in 2003 by Fox Chapel Publishing.

In addition to writing and carving, Tom conducts seminars and classes across the United States, with instructional classes at his home studio. Most of the time he can be found answering questions and providing guidance on the decoy carving forum, *www.decoycarvingforum.com*. This is a collective group of carvers from the United States and ten other countries that actively engages in discussion about promoting the art form of carving decoys. If not at the forum, he is most likely with his loving wife, roaming the scenic western states of Idaho and Montana in pursuit of waterfowl and wildlife.

Foreword

When I saw Tom's work for the first time, I told my boys, Jett and Jude, "Here comes another one. Listen and take heed; this carver will leave an imprint on our world—the world of decoy carving." In my eyes, Tom Matus will continue to excel in the art that was begun by the American Indians, over 1,000 years ago. Tom Matus is like all of us who can't wait for the next show. I long for his imprint on this art we love so much, but like all good things that don't last, his presence is a feeling. He longs to grab all of the positives in life, and, when we part, I feel an emptiness that says, "We could have shared so much more together, and I look forward to our next meeting."

To quote a famous writer, "No one knows who cast out the first decoy, but its ripple has never ceased to widen." I am sure Tom Matus wants to be one of these ripples. You can tell after being with Tom that he has a genuine love of the decoy. Lem Ward once told me, "You know, Tan, some of us love the decoy more than others." And Tom is one who does.

The decoy is tangible and collective. It fits well in an old gunning camp or on the desk of the President. As art, it is hunted and auctioned. When it is retired, it is not forgotten; instead, it is put on a pedestal and admired. As a lost and found derelict, it is cherished instead of abandoned. We as humans should be that well respected.

The decoy is part of our heritage. I want to be counted in the tally of contributing carvers to that heritage. I believe Tom Matus wants this also. If history counts the ones who care, Tom Matus will be in. He is young, energetic, prolific, and talented, but most of all, he is generous. I admire a person who shares, and thankfully Tom is willing to share his gift with the world.

—*Tan Brunet*

Rainbow of the Swamp
Through the maze of moss-draped trees,
He glides with the grace of a gazelle.

His cry shrieks and echoes,
As rung from a seasoned bell.

His home is the enchanted swamp,
Where the cypress and tupelo grow.

Dressed with the colors of the rainbow,
A thing of beauty, with an elegant glow.

As a phoenix he emerges from the murk,
With his mate in their bobbling gait.

He is a gift from God above,
Please be kind, for man's sake.

—Tan Brunet

Introduction

Contemporary Antique Hunting Decoys—The Contemporary Collectible

The hunting decoy is truly an American folk art form, with origins that can be traced back 2,000 years to American Indians who lived in what is now Nevada. As the United States grew, and with it the demand for waterfowl to feed the populace, hunters used live birds, bait, and handcarved wooden decoys as tools to gather food.

During the Golden Age of Waterfowling, following the passage of the Migratory Bird Treaty Act of 1918, the popularity of wooden decoys grew. But as technology developed, wooden hunting decoys were replaced by plastic ones. Regarded as pieces of "tired old hunting equipment," many vintage wooden decoys were thrown away or destroyed. Those that survived experienced new life after World War II as people began to recognize their historic significance.

Decoy collecting started in the 1950s and soared in popularity during the 1980s. Each flyway or gunning area developed its own style of decoy. In the upper Chesapeake Bay, the Havre de Grace style, with its rounded bottoms, was popular. Carvers in the Illinois River area favored long, narrow bodies with fine paint. New Jersey carvers crafted hollow cedar decoys with inletted lead weights. Old-time carvers like A. Elmer Crowell, Joe Lincoln, Ira Hudson, and Lem and Steve Ward became well known for their work.

As the demand for high-quality antique decoys increased, prices skyrocketed. It was not uncommon to see decoys selling in the six-figure range at auction. In fact, an A. Elmer Crowell preening pintail from Cape Cod, Massachusetts, sold for a record $319,000 in 1987. It has since resold for $801,500. These prices put most of the quality decoys out of the price range of most people.

As an alternative, the contemporary antique decoy was born. It gave the collector the opportunity to own a decoy with the style and characteristics of its forebears without paying the price for an actual antique. At first, some contemporary antique decoys were so well made that the copies were often passed off as originals by unscrupulous individuals. It is said that even some of the experts were fooled.

In response, carvers of new contemporary antique decoys began to add their own design and carving styles to the vintage decoys they were emulating. They exaggerated certain features, blended carving styles, brightened paint, and added their own personal flair to the classic decoy style. In doing so, they created their own niche in the decoy collecting world. These contemporary antique decoys complement the finest vintage decoy collections, and no collection is complete without one.

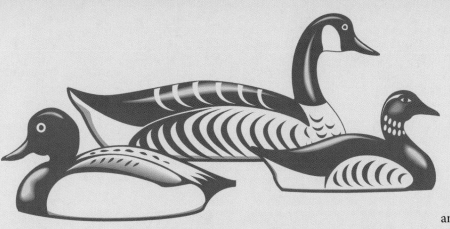

What should you look for when selecting a contemporary antique decoy? Here are some criteria:

Form: Is the style true to its roots—Delaware River, Cape Cod, Illinois River, or other? Is the spirit of the original hunting decoy visible? Does the decoy have the right proportions?

Finish: What sort of patina does the decoy have? Is the finish soft or dry? Is the paint oil or acrylic? Does the distressing look natural or is it methodically applied?

Functionality: Does the decoy float? Is it durable enough to be used for hunting? Is it really a hunting decoy?

Artistic Creativity: Has the carver employed enough creativity to distinguish his decoy from the original, making it unique and not merely a copy?

Price: Is the price in line with the features listed? Is it affordable?

After weighing each criteria, it comes down to this: If you like it, buy it! (See the photo on page xii for an example of how to use this rating system.)

The future is bright for the contemporary antique decoy, and the carvers are to be complimented on their creativity in re-stylizing classic American decoys. Whether you are a new carver exploring this exciting new style of decoy or a veteran carver looking for a change of pace, this book will prove to be an invaluable resource. Here you will find the basics of carving and painting a stylized contemporary decoy as well as detailed instructions for aging techniques and surface preparations. Inspirational examples of both antique and contemporary antique duck decoys from around the country fill the pages of the following gallery section, giving readers a visual reference of the different carving styles from such diverse regions as the upper Chesapeake Bay, the Delaware River area, the Great Lakes, New England, North Carolina, and California.

The development of the contemporary antique decoy is an important step in the evolution of the wooden decoy. This book sets the stage for new categories of marketable decoys. Upon this foundation, carvers can let their imaginations take wing.

—*Kyan Kraus*

Kyan Kraus is a vice president of the Ohio Decoy Collectors and Carvers Association (ODCCA) and an organizer of the ODCCA's annual decoy show held the third weekend of March in Westlake, Ohio. He is also a frequent contributor to the antiques section of *Decoycarvingforum.com* and *Ohiowaterfowler.com*. His interest in hunting—he hunts the Sandusky Bay; the marshes of Lake Erie and Long Point, Ontario; Maine; and the Delmarva Peninsula—led him to collecting decoys, which he has been doing for about twenty years.

Here's Kyan's evaluation of this pair of contemporary antique green-winged teal decoys made in 2004 by Pete Peterson from Capeville, Virginia, using the rating criteria outlined on page xi. The maximum possible points for each of the five categories is 10.

Form: Lower Virginia, North Carolina, Back Bay area, somewhat Dudley-esque, True to form. Proportionally excellent. 10 points.

Finish: Soft patina, appears to have been rottenstoned. Soft finish, oil paint, no distressing. 9 points.

Functionality: Excellent floating ability—no listing, pitching, or yawing. Appears durable. Definitely a hunting decoy. 10 points.

Artistic Creativity: Stylized sweeping neck and head. Paint applied in a manner consistent with the decoy. 10 points.

Price: Affordable, but on the expensive side. 7 points.

Total points: 46 out of a possible 50. This pair of decoys is worthy of a place in anyone's collection.

**Contemporary Antique Pair of Mallards
by Ira "Steve" Skees, Onley, Virginia, circa 2003.**

In 1992, the original pair of decoys by the Caines brothers sold for what was then a record price of $285,000. The decoys were from the estate of Jean Yawkey, former owner of the Boston Red Sox.

These decoys were made as contemporary hunting decoys and have been hunted over several times by this collector. The quality and style are timeless, making them just as effective as a hunting lure as the originals carved in the early 1900s.

**Contemporary Antique Mallard Hen
by Tom Matus, Boise, Idaho, circa 2002.**

This cork decoy, in the style of "Shang" Wheeler, Stratford, Connecticut, is from Tom's personal hunting rig. Nicely carved and painted in oil, it represents his first attempt at a Shang-Wheeler-style decoy.

**Antique Humpback Pintail
by an unknown maker, Crisfield, Maryland, circa 1925.**

This decoy has a rich patina and beautiful scratch paint with an unbroken tail. The style is classic with its humpback, elongated tail, and original rusted chain ballast weight.

**Contemporary Antique Ruddy Duck
by Mark McNair, Craddocksville, Virginia, 1990.**

This diminutive decoy is done in the style of Lee
Dudley, one of North Carolina's most prolific carvers.
It is neatly carved and represents the famous Dudley
ruddy duck in the Shelburne Museum.

**Contemporary Antique Hooded Merganser
by Reggie Birch, Chincoteague, Virginia, circa 1994.**

This contemporary stylized decoy from the Eastern Shore
represents one of the most famous areas in waterfowl
gunning history—Cobb Island. Most decoys from Cobb Island
were washed away in a 1933 hurricane.

Contemporary Antique American Wigeon by Jim Schmiedlin, Bradford Woods, Pennsylvania, 1997.

This decoy from Jim's personal hunting rig has the look and style of classic American folk art. Its oil paint is beautifully blended, and it has a patina reflecting its years of use as a hunting decoy. Prized for their meticulous paint and fine detail, Schmiedlin decoys are highly desired trophies in the collecting world and are often impossible to obtain because Jim sells only a few a year from his personal hunting rig.

Contemporary Antique Pintail Drake by Cameron McIntyre, Eastern Shore, Virginia, circa 1998.

This beautifully surfaced decoy is Cameron's interpretation of the classic Blair decoys from the Philadelphia school of carvers. The originals were used on the Delaware River between Trenton, New Jersey, and Philadelphia and also at the oldest duck hunting club in North America—Ohio's Winous Point Shooting Club on Sandusky Bay, off southwestern Lake Erie.

**Contemporary Antique Red-Breasted Merganser
by Mark McNair, Craddocksville, Virginia, circa 1993.**

This flat-bottomed decoy has a beautiful hairy head, an aged
surface, and a style reminiscent of its older counterpart.

**Contemporary Antique Red-Breasted Merganser Drake
by Tom Matus, Boise, Idaho, 1996.**

This mixed-style decoy features a modern head carved from tupelo
and a cedar body with a slightly raised grain. Painted in mixed
media, oil, and acrylics, it is from the collection of Deborah Matus.

**Antique Canvasback Drake
by John Graham Body and John "Daddy" Holly Head,
Havre de Grace, Maryland, circa 1860.**

This 19th-century decoy retains some of its original paint. It is unique because it is representative of a "married" piece—a piece where the head and the body come from two different makers. The decoy shown here was probably used in one of the great sneak boat rigs of the Susquehanna Flats in the market gunning era of the late 1800s.

Contemporary Antique Monhegan Island Eider Drake by an unknown maker, New England, year unknown.

This beautiful, stylized eider with a mussel in its mouth is done in the classic Monhegan Island style.

Antique Oversized Black Duck by George Boyd, Seabrook, New Hampshire, circa 1890.

With classic New England styling from New Hampshire's most famous carver, this decoy is easily recognized by its almost cartoonish-looking head. It is in excellent condition for being more than 100 years old.

**Contemporary Antique Black Duck
by George Strunk, Glendora, New Jersey, circa 2004.**

This hollow-carved decoy with delicate paint was included in the decoys of the Atlantic Flyway exhibit at the Smithsonian Institution in Washington, D.C., in the summer of 2004. Its long, narrow body is representative of classic Delaware River styling.

**Contemporary Antique Blue-Winged Teal Drake
by Jim Schmiedlin, Bradford Woods, Pennsylvania, 1999.**

This delicately painted decoy is from Jim's hunting rig. Schmiedlin decoys are identifiable by their beautiful flowing lines, rich patinas, and precise details. His name and address is painted on the bottom of each decoy along with the words "Reward for return," and the hunting history of the decoy written in pencil, such as "Sandusky Bay 2000."

Schmiedlin decoys are highly prized because he represents the last of a dying breed of "layout" hunters who hunt canvasbacks, redheads, and bluebill on the open waters of the Great Lakes, gunning over massive, handcarved wooden rigs while lying on their backs in pumpkin-seed-style boats.

**Antique Palm Frond Pintails
from a California gunning club
by an unknown maker, circa 1950.**

These decoys, representative of the
classic California decoy, have their
original lines and weights. The mere
fact that they still exist after 55 years
is a testament to the maker.

**Contemporary Antique Pair of Delaware-River-Style Canvasbacks
by Bob White, Tullytown, Pennsylvania, circa 1990.**

These decoys feature raised wing carvings and extraordinary detail,
characteristics of the classic Delaware-River-style decoy. Bob's distinguishing
triangular lead weights with the "Bob White Quail" are attached to the bottoms of
these decoys. White, considered to be among the last of the old-school carvers, is
known for his fine carving and wonderful paint work, making his decoys popular
with collectors.

**Contemporary Antique Old Squaw
by Tom Matus, Boise, Idaho, circa 2004.**

This old squaw is a modified breast preener with the style and flare of a New England decoy. Made from cedar, it is painted in mixed media and heavily stressed and aged. It comes from the collection of Deborah Matus.

**Contemporary Antique Wood Duck
by Tom Matus, Boise, Idaho, circa 2005.**

The form and style of this decoy is more contemporary than most, but it is aged and antiqued to look as if it has been used for many years. Made of hollow cedar and painted with mixed media, this decoy comes from the collection of Deborah Matus.

**Contemporary Antique Pair of Mallards
by Tom Matus, Boise, Idaho, circa 2002.**

These birds made of hollow cedar are painted in oil and have
beautiful combing reminiscent of the finest makers of gunning
decoys. They come from the author's personal hunting rig.

**Antique Canada Goose
by Ira Hudson, Chincoteague, Virginia, circa 1930.**

Classic hissing style by one of the Eastern Shore's
most famous carvers features a solid body.

**Antique Canada Goose
by Harry V. Shourds, Tuckerton,
New Jersey, circa 1890.**

This resting-head-style decoy from the Barnegat,
New Jersey, school of carvers has an inletted lead weight. This goose
was purchased directly from Johnny Hillman in November 1969, and this
information is marked in pencil on the tail. In 2003, Mr. Hillman's collection
was sold at auction for $2.7 million, a record at that time. Included in that
collection were two Harry Shourds geese—a swimming head version that
sold for $105,000 and the famous hissing head that sold for $204,000.

CHAPTER 1

CARVING THE DECOY   AGING THE WOOD   PAINTING   ANTIQUING

GETTING STARTED

The wood duck is one of the most colorful and animated ducks we can observe in the wild. Because of its distinctive colors and behavior, it is also one of the most challenging birds to create. As you go through the steps, attention to detail and the use of your reference material will be important parts of the process. Keep your references handy and readily available so that during both the carving and the painting phases you can access them. In this chapter, we'll look at reference materials, the characteristics of the wood duck, wood selection for your decoy, the basic tools, and the use and creation of patterns.

Gathering live bird reference materials

Reference materials can come in a variety of forms: Photographs, study skins, study casts, and your own field notes are just a few of the different types (see **Figures 1.1** to **1.10** for reference photos with field notes). While a combination of the different materials can work very well, gathering your own field notes is by far one of the best ways to learn about your subject.

The wood duck has many field markings and characteristics that a carver can use to his advantage. When evaluating the bird on the water, I use—and highly recommend—a notepad and drawing tablet to remind me of field markings I want to incorporate into the decoy. I see the head as a great opportunity to add individual flare and artistic expression. The elongated body, long tail, and white barring will aid in creating some overall flow. We are trying to incorporate all of these features into the decoy without overdoing it. Thus, we can get away from the micrometers and exact measurements that competitions have forced us to abide by, which is the very reason that we are making this decoy. With this style of decoy, you have the ability to exaggerate and add feeling to the bird, making this project a *fun* challenge.

Figure 1.1. Notice the angle of the primaries and tail—they are almost parallel.

Figure 1.2. Wood ducks have an interesting feather flow on the side pocket where the vermiculation overlaps the black and white barring.

Figure 1.3. This closeup shows the details of the side pocket and the belly area.

Figure 1.4. Observe how the leading edge of the primaries (bluish white) forms a triangle from an overhead view.

Figure 1.5. This closeup shows the details of the primaries and the tertials.

Figure 1.6. Pay close attention to the white markings on the head. They change with the posture and attitude of the duck.

Figure 1.7. Note the angle of the tail and the primaries in this alert, proud pose.

Characteristics of the wood duck

Knowing the habitat and behaviors of your subject will help you truly capture the essence of the animal in your carving. The following information should provide you with a good starting point for your wood duck.

The overcast morning starts with a thin mist covering the marsh, and, as the morning sun starts to burn off the haze, a defined silhouette appears in the distance that can only be a wood duck drake. You hear the *wheeeekkk whhhheeeeekkk* of the female as she strides out in front, slowly gliding across the water. Wood ducks are very mystical in the wild, and they are some of the most colorful and elegant ducks in North America, making them an easy choice for an antique decoy.

Wood ducks, *Aix sponsa*, are tree dwellers and favor the forest marshes and river bottoms. Their food source consists largely of vegetable matter and some aquatic insects, the insects composing a lower percentage of their diet. Wood ducks are often spotted and identified by their erratic flight, head-to-body posture, and wide tail. They bob their heads during flight like no other duck; they are sometimes confused with the wigeon because of the abrupt breast line and white belly. When floating, the wood duck drake can be identified by its bright colors and its distinct head shape and markings. The white markings on the head and the body are a dead giveaway. The hen is also very attractive, sporting mottled feathers, soft browns, and a striking white eye patch. Her appearance allows her to hide very well during nesting periods. She nests in the same area year after year near where she was hatched. She will lay 10 to 15 white eggs in the hollow of a tree in a secluded area of the swamp.

Figure 1.8. This angle shows the details on the tertials, the primaries, and the upper rump.

Figure 1.9. Here is a good shot of the head and breast.

Figure 1.10. Take note of this head detail, especially the size of the eye and the bill coloration. Also notice that the upper white crest is not complete.

Wood selection

Now that we have a bird in mind, we need to discuss what type of wood we are going to use. My selection of wood is white cedar (see **Figure 1.11**). This wood is soft, straight grained, and light colored. It works well with hand or power tools, and it takes paint very well. Northern white cedar is unfortunately not as plentiful as it once was—it has been used for various building products—and wood cut to size for decoys can be difficult to find. Some companies cater to carvers who want decoy-sized wood, which is a great asset. Check the Resources section on page 108 for more information.

This project also takes advantage of wood that has a few knots and imperfections. The knots and small splits or wormholes will add character to the decoy, as if these effects happened during its life of use. Be careful, however, because too many knots will detract from the decoy and make the painting difficult. There is a fine line between too many and not enough. Trial and error will be your best bet. After completing a few decoys with knots in them, you will have a better idea of what to look for prior to cutting out the decoy.

Pine would be my second selection for this project because the grain lines and the growth rings provide a good look (see **Figure 1.12**). I have found the pine tar and pitch that leak from the wood to be a major distraction and problem to work around. Over time, the yellow color of the pitch will seep through the wood and create a nasty color under any areas of light-colored paint on the finished bird. I recommend using wood that has been dried to about 10 percent moisture content and has been sitting for a time. You do not want this aspect of the wood to ruin the bird after you have put a good amount of work into it.

Figure 1.11. One of my favorite woods for carving duck decoys is white cedar. Its softness and straight grain make it very easy to work with.

Figure 1.12. Although the pine tar and pitch can be a distraction, pine can be a good choice for your decoy because of the character that its grain lines and growth rings add.

MASTER TIP

Making Your Decoy Look Older
Some carvers may like to take this old-style decoy to extremes and use an older wood with more knots and some areas of dry rot to make their decoy look even older. The best part of making a decoy with knots and rotten areas is that you never know where these areas will end up on the carving, which adds to the creativity.

Tupelo (see **Figure 1.13**) and American linden (basswood) are my least favorite woods for this type of project. These woods have tight grain lines, fewer knots, and minimal imperfections. Knots are seldom found, and, when they are included, they are usually very small and do not add to the look I am trying to achieve. However, I have found that these woods do sand very well, and, after they have been sealed and sanded with 180 grit, you have a great surface for oil paints.

If you order a large amount of any carving wood, it is best stored out of the sunlight where there is minimal temperature and humidity change. Rapid changes in climate will cause the wood to crack and dry out. Sometimes the wood will even become very hard to carve. I recommend that you look at the relative humidity index for your area and order accordingly. Many times, the wood will be best stored in a cool, dry place. Waxing or painting the ends of the pieces will minimize the end cracking.

Figure 1.13. Because of its tendency to have minimal imperfections, tupelo is less suitable for this style of decoy than pine or white cedar. However, if you prefer to try a clearer wood, tupelo is relatively easy to work with hand or power tools.

MASTER TIP

Selecting Wood
When selecting wood, keep these rules of thumb in mind:

White cedar should be light and white with straight grain and should have knots smaller than a dime.

Pine should be slightly yellow with minimal knots. Carry a knife, take a sliver of wood, and smell the sliver. The wood should be fresh, not stale.

Tupelo, like cedar, should be light and white with no knots.

Regardless of the type of wood you prefer, always buy wood from a reputable dealer.

Tools

In the past, I have used power tools to rough out some of my decoys; however, I will be using hand tools in this book. Power tools require a much larger investment, whereas hand tools are less expensive and more appropriate for this style of decoy. I have grown accustomed to less dust and to the larger chips that are taken off with drawknives and rasps. However, just because I am using hand tools here does not mean that you cannot substitute a power tool. If you have one and are accustomed to that power tool, feel free to use it wherever you find it comfortable and appropriate.

I also find that I have a better feel for the bird when I am using hand tools. There is something about the use of a hand tool when working on a traditional gunning decoy that makes the whole process more real. That pleasant aroma of the cedar and the gentle removal of the wood make it more personable. I feel more relaxed and can see where the bird is going without wood being removed too quickly.

But, believe me, wood will come off quickly enough with all of the hand tools mentioned in this section. I also believe that you should use the largest tool for the job to help create smooth transitions and equal contours throughout your decoy. I like long, smooth strokes that remove wood in an even manner. A small knife leaves divots that are not true to the form of the bird I see. The only power tools that I used on the decoy in this book were the band saw to cut the blank and the drill press to hollow the decoy. The use of these tools is obvious for the time-saving benefits they add.

The list of hand tools includes drawknives, spokeshaves, pattern maker's rasps, carving knives, and specialty tools. On this and the following pages, I've included notes on each type of tool and some of their uses.

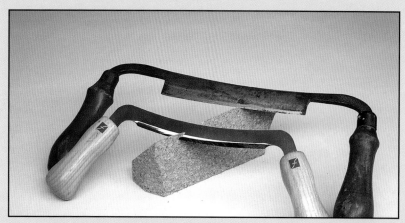

Drawknives: Having a few different sizes is beneficial (see **Figure 1.14**). Larger drawknives will allow you to remove larger quantities of wood. Smaller ones will allow you to get into tighter areas.

Figure 1.14. These are two of the drawknives I use to start the body when large amounts of wood need to be removed. The larger drawknife has better handles and expedites the process of roughing out the decoy. The smaller drawknife will remove wood that is critical to the body shape and anatomy.

Spokeshaves: A spokeshave will minimize the amount of rough sanding that you have to do and will provide a nice symmetrical outcome. Master carvers used to use these instead of sandpaper and go from this point straight to painting (see **Figure 1.15**).

Figure 1.15. Once the decoy has been roughed into shape with rasps and drawknives, I use spokeshaves to smooth out the bird, which will minimize the amount of hand sanding I have to do.

Rasps: Rasps are used in tighter areas to remove wood and to shape (see **Figure 1.16**). They will allow you to shape the body and head union for better flow. Rasps will remove wood very quickly.

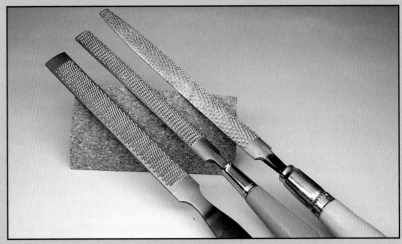

Figure 1.16. These are my three favorite rasps that I use when roughing. The three rasps have rounded backs and are used in areas around the rump and in the neck area.

Rifflers: Rifflers are smaller rasps that will remove wood in extremely tight areas (see **Figure 1.17**). I use them for final shaping and touch-up work. A round Surform rasp and a Microplane plane are also useful for final shaping.

Figure 1.17. A set of shaping tools is inexpensive and should be added to your tool list. I use rounded rasps and rifflers around the areas that require a concave cut. The riffler is extremely helpful around the upper rump and the head.

Gouges: Gouges have become more and more frequently used for my removal of wood. I like using the smaller palm gouges and a glove with padding to remove wood because I can feel the wood being removed and can go slower when I need control. I can also accelerate when I need large quantities of wood removed. Gouges are easy to keep sharp, reasonably priced, and readily available in most carving stores (see **Figure 1.18**).

Figure 1.18. When I work around the bill, primaries, and tail, I use this set of gouges. Any of the name-brand gouges will work, as long as you maintain an extremely sharp edge and work with the grain. I prefer a brand of gouges that fits my hand well, which helps to prevent fatigue.

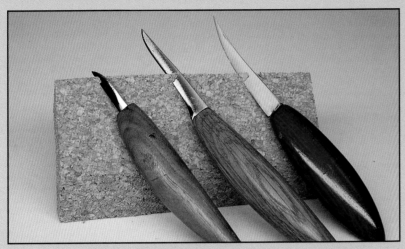

Figure 1.19. Here are my favorite three knives, from left to right, the small detailer, a large detailer with rounded tip, and a Cajun tupelo knife, which allows me to get into small, detailed areas with that small pointed tip. The other two knives are for detailing.

Figure 1.20. These tools are specialty tools that will come in handy throughout the carving process. From left to right: a 1" Forstner bit to hollow out the decoy; a small Surform rasp for removing glue; a bow sander to help achieve a smooth, round decoy; and a larger Surform rasp, which helps to remove large amounts of wood.

MASTER TIP

Sharpening Your Carving Tools

It's extremely important to keep your carving tools sharp. Working with a dull blade is hazardous and will increase your chances of cutting yourself. I like to keep a leather strop handy when I'm carving with knives and gouges. Every 10 to 15 minutes, I strop the blade to maintain a sharp, honed edge. I apply a small amount of aluminum oxide to the leather as a polishing compound.

Knives: A few different sizes of knives will give you the selection that you need (see **Figure 1.19**). If you feel comfortable with one knife and like using it, feel free to use that one, but a variety of shaped blades will be helpful. Be sure to keep your blades razor sharp so that carving is less stressful as well as less labor intensive. It is vital that every carver learn how to maintain an edge on his/her knives.

Forstner bits: I use the Forstner bits for wood removal during the hollowing process (see **Figure 1.20**). Again, it is good to have a variety of sizes, but, for your first project, I recommend a 1"-size drill. Use your drill or drill press at a moderate speed of about 1,500 rpm.

Flat Surform rasps: The Surform rasps create a neat texture and allow ease of sculpting the wood. Replacement blades are readily available, and, if you dull them on glue joints and knots, you can acquire spare blades at a reasonable cost. Also, these are great tools for general shaping.

Bow sander: Most bow sanders are homemade, but a few commercial sanders are available on the market today. Using this tool will aid in making a round, symmetrical bird if you want to sand it. I recommend a 40-, 80-, and 120-grit bow sander. Never go beyond 120 when sanding this style of decoy. You will want to see some of the tool marks.

Vise: This is one of the most important tools to have in your shop. There are a few ways to get around not having a vise, but, in the long run, you will need to obtain one. This one is called the work station, made by The Duck Blind (see **Figure 1.21**). It is a 360-degree vise that allows circular movement while working on the decoy, and it has a slot that lets the desired carving become perpendicular to the vise, which gives the carver access to the bottom areas of the decoy (see Steps 29 and 30 on page 39). It makes the rough carving process much easier and allows you to use two hands for detail without any loss of control with the carving tools. Once you use this style of vise, you will wonder how you ever carved without one. You may also consider building a horse head vise, which is another valuable tool that will secure the decoy body while carving.

Figure 1.21. This handy 360-degree vise allows circular movement while working on the decoy. The large backing nut on top keeps the carving on the work station securely. I have mounted the vise to a grinder floor stand and then to the concrete floor. I filled in around the base with anti-vibration foam flooring to allow extended standing time on the concrete and to help protect my tools if I drop one on the floor; the soft material hopefully minimizes the damage.

Using the pattern

Just because a pattern is provided with this project does not ensure that your decoy—or, for that matter, any others you create—will turn out like the one shown in this book. A pattern is just a starting point, and once you make the pattern a few times, creating changes and alterations, your decoy should start to take on your style. Each time you make the decoy, I recommend that you write the date and anything you altered or changed on the pattern. This way, the next time you cut out this decoy, you can make the appropriate changes on the new decoy. Most of the time, when making a decoy a second or third time, I will throw the original pattern away and just keep the newer pattern in my files.

To start off this pattern, I have selected a swimming pose, with the bird outstretched as if he were moving out and swimming away from the viewer. I want to add life and a "look" to the decoy as if he were startled, just looking with concern and getting away from the observer without taking flight. I have witnessed this behavior many times while hunting and bird-watching. It's a common look that I really enjoy, and it seems typical of this species.

With this pattern, please feel free to alter and adjust things that you observe and want to add. This is the only way that a bird can reflect your style. For example, try adjusting the crest, bill angle, neck-to-body angle, and tail angle. All of these could be changed to suit your preference. Altering them will also change the attitude of the bird.

Creating a pattern

Many carvers I talk with seem to hit a hurdle when it comes to making or designing their own patterns. A pattern is all about creativity and practice. Trust me, the first design any of the top carvers sketch is not their final one—not even close. You should consider the pencil and pad your ally when you are in the process of making patterns. Too many people overlook this process when they are trying to be creative. Try to inject your feelings into the bird from this initial step, and you will gain a great respect for your creation.

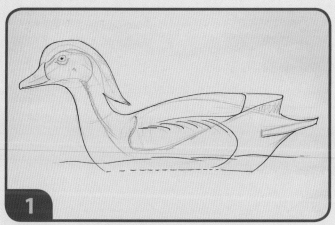

In this first photo, I refined a field observation sketch that was marginal, incorporating the notes I took during observation. Notice that I added the wing and skull structure to the bird in this first attempt. I will step back from the sketch and make notes for changes I want to make.

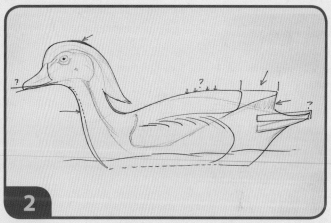

Now that I have an initial pattern (not close to putting this on wood yet), I will make more changes to refine the look I want. Starting from the front, I noted the following problem areas: the bill angle should change, the crest had a flat spot, the neck appeared too wide for the pose, the high spot on the back was off and needed to move, the length of the exposed primary was off, and the tail angle should be altered. This is how I see the bird. This is undoubtedly the most creative part of making the pattern because you can change anything at this point.

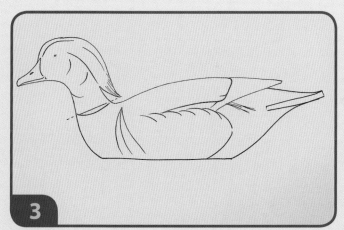

I am getting closer to the pattern I want. Changing the tail angle and the bill angle helps to define the look. A couple more changes and I should be all set. During this process, I use a black marker to make a few lines to see if the bird still looks like the wood duck I envision. I can go back and add more bells and whistles, but this should be a simplistic design, and I am starting to achieve that.

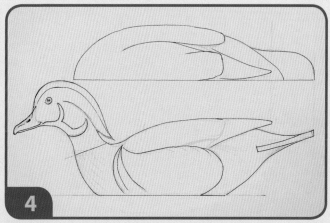

I am now confident that this pattern will get me close enough to the swimming wood duck I envisioned. The next page shows the final pattern that I will be using to cut the wood duck decoy.

Enlarge pattern 110%.

1.000

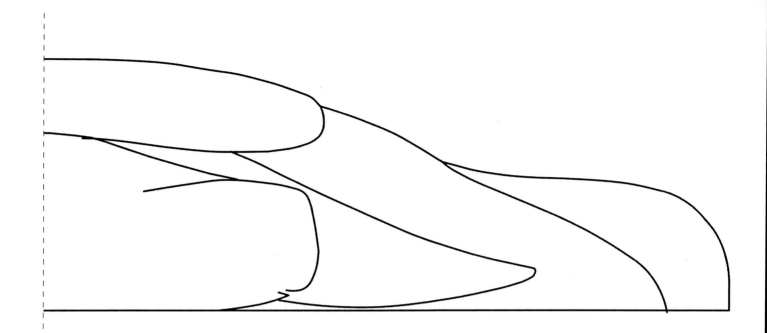

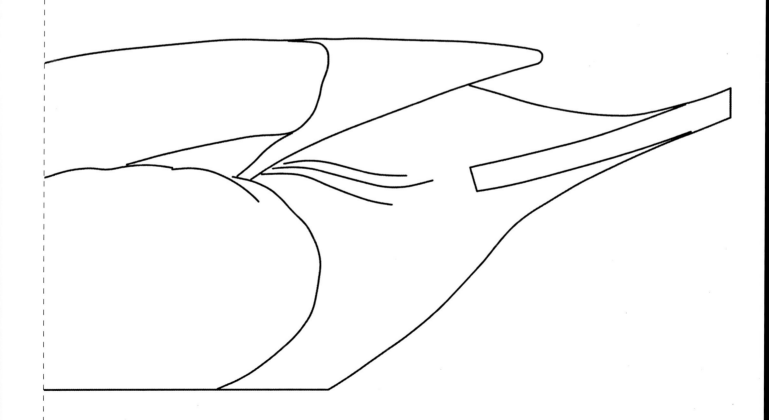

Transferring the pattern

The wood we chose for this project is white cedar. Because we're making a hollowed-out antique decoy, the body of the decoy will be made from two pieces of wood. The first piece, which will be the bottom part of the decoy, should measure 13⅝" x 6" x 1½". The second piece, which will be the top part of the decoy, should measure 13⅝" x 6" x 2½". A third piece of wood, measuring 5⅜" x 2" x 4¼", is needed for the head.

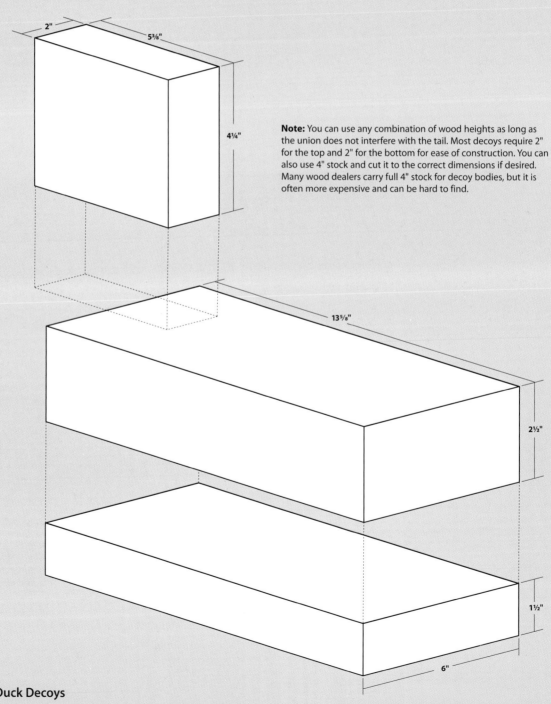

Note: You can use any combination of wood heights as long as the union does not interfere with the tail. Most decoys require 2" for the top and 2" for the bottom for ease of construction. You can also use 4" stock and cut it to the correct dimensions if desired. Many wood dealers carry full 4" stock for decoy bodies, but it is often more expensive and can be hard to find.

Tracing the head pattern

Now we're ready to put the pattern on the wood. I've chosen some used stock that I had lying around my shop. Because the head is small, you can often find a good piece of wood that may have been left over from a previous project. A pushpin works well to hold the head pattern in place while you are tracing the pattern onto the wood.

Cut out the head pattern from heavy cardboard and place it on the cedar with the bill orientated with the grain of the wood. I use a pushpin to hold the pattern in place while I trace the pattern onto the head stock.

Here I traced the pattern with a black magic marker to see it better and to get it ready to cut out on the band saw.

MASTER TIP

Aligning the Bill with the Grain
To maintain strength and durability, the bill must be aligned with the grain. Do not align the bottom of the neck with the bottom of your stock. If you align the bottom of the neck with your stock, carving the bill will be extremely difficult, and the bill could actually chip or break off.

Tracing the body pattern

Now that the pattern for the head has been drawn on the wood, let's do the same thing for the body. As we discussed, this bird will be hollow, so we need to cut out the decoy from two pieces of wood: a 2½" section, which is the top section, and a 1½" section, which is the bottom section. These measurements allow the glue joint to be above the waterline when the decoy is finished. It also helps with the hollowing-out process; when I'm ready, all I have to do is unscrew the two pieces of wood and start to hollow out the decoy with the drill press.

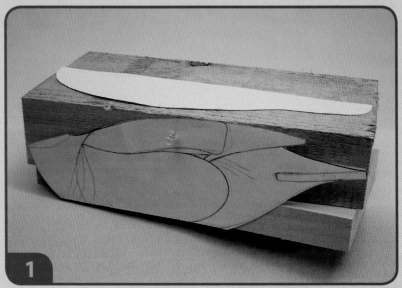

1

Align the two pieces of wood. The grain lines should form a circle. I line up the pattern so that the primaries are positioned with the grain. For instruction purposes, I shifted the top section of the wood so that you can see where the glue joint will be. The two sections will be realigned when I cut out the bird.

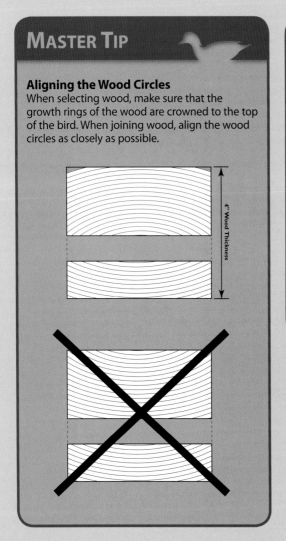

MASTER TIP

Aligning the Wood Circles
When selecting wood, make sure that the growth rings of the wood are crowned to the top of the bird. When joining wood, align the wood circles as closely as possible.

4" Wood Thickness

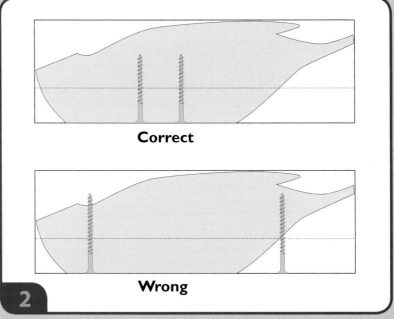

Correct

Wrong

2

Check the alignment and join these two sections of wood with two 3" drywall screws. I countersink the screws so they do not hang up on the band saw table when I am cutting out the body. It's important to place the screws at the maximum height of the pattern, where they will not come in contact with the band saw blade. Any contact that the blade makes with the screws will completely ruin the blade and is a safety hazard. I also use my mounting plate for the work station to measure the distance between the screws. This way, the same holes that I used to hold the wood together during the cut can be used for mounting the decoy to the work station. Whenever possible, try to minimize the number of holes in the bird so that there is less possibility of water entering the hollow cavity. Once we've joined the sections and transferred the pattern, we'll proceed to cutting out the head and body so that we can start to rough out the decoy.

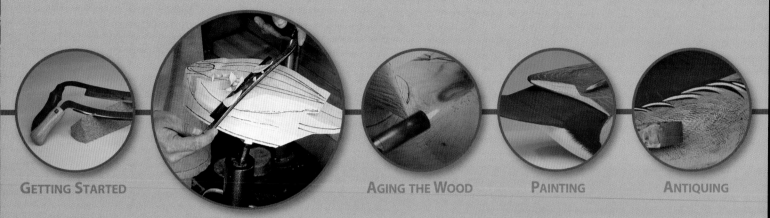

CHAPTER 2

GETTING STARTED · AGING THE WOOD · PAINTING · ANTIQUING

CARVING THE DECOY

When cutting out the decoy, you will want to make sure that you simply follow the line and leave a small amount of the magic marker. I use a band saw; some carvers use a hatchet or drawknife while the wood is locked in a vise. I am a firm believer in the fact that each good decoy comes from a well-cut-out blank. You should not have to go back and try to level your band saw cuts. These are strategic cuts, and they will affect the overall profile of the decoy. When carving your decoy, take your time. Much of this process, with the exception of the band saw and the drill press, will be conducted with good old-fashioned hand tools. When making an antique-style decoy, I believe that some of the traditional methods should be incorporated into the construction process. Modern high-speed grinders could be used, but I do not feel that they fit in with this project. If you are using a knife, try to remove as much wood as possible with the largest knife available.

CUTTING OUT THE HEAD

Cutting out the head is very important. You should make mental notes on where you left a little extra wood so that, when you take measurements, the head comes out correctly. You may also want to consider a ¼" blade so that turning is easier on the saw as well as the cut. The bill should be cut to the exact length so that there is a good measuring point.

Prior to making any cuts, I always make sure that the band saw blade is perpendicular to the table. I have a metal framer's square within easy access to make sure the blade is properly aligned. The first time you cut out a bird with a tilted table, you will remember this hint. I also double-check that the screws are countersunk and not sticking out of the bottom of the bird. If the screws are sticking out, they will hit the push guide on the table and cause problems.

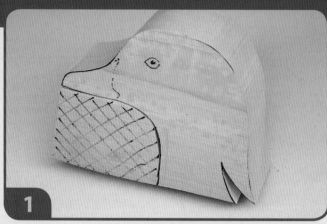

The first cut on the head removes the extra wood from the crown area. Notice that I have left the extra wood underneath the bill (the crosshatched area). I leave this section on when cutting the top profile of the head as a safety measure. I do not advise cutting the top view without having this piece intact, since this would create a major safety concern. The blade can catch the wood, pulling it out of your hands and pulling your fingers into the blade path, so be very careful when approaching this area.

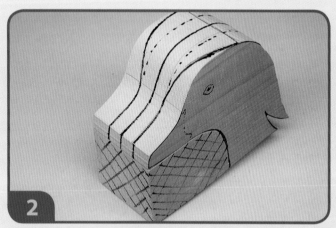

Here, I added the centerline and the quarter lines, which divide the head into quarters, to the top. This will give me the rough dimensions of the crown and allow me to plan the next few cuts. I also measured the bill and placed that width on either side of the centerline to give me a feel for the bill area. These are all of the lines required at this point.

Remove the front and back portions from the head. As I mentioned earlier, you can remove this material with the head in a vise using a hatchet or a drawknife if you don't want to use the band saw.

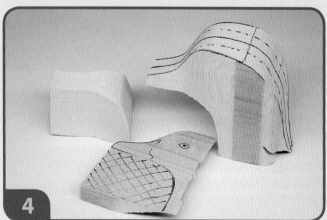

The last two pieces have been removed. The head is completely cut out.

MASTER TIP

Band Saw Blade Selection
It's very important to choose the right band saw blade so that your blade does not track in the grain lines. Because wood grain has areas of both hard and soft wood, the blade reacts differently to these areas. A blade that is thinner than the grain lines will tend to follow the lines of softer wood, making it difficult to cut along the pattern lines. A blade that is thicker than the grain lines will straddle the hard and soft grains, making it easier to cut along the pattern lines. A thinner blade is used for the head in most cases. I recommend using a ¼" x 4" tpi blade for the head cutout and a ½" x 4" tpi blade for the body.

CUTTING OUT THE BODY

Now let's cut out the body. Notice that there is a one-inch mark across the middle of the back. This mark is a stopping point so that when we cut out the side profile, the wood does not fall apart and the two pieces of wood remain intact while we are cutting. Some other carvers hot-glue these sections; some tape them. I find stopping short more efficient.

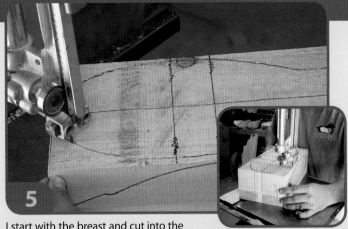

I start with the breast and cut into the stop-cut line I marked across the back of the bird. This is about a 1" mark that I draw across the top of each bird to remind me that I have to stop and back out the blade. I back out the blade with the saw in the "off" position because removing the blade from the cut will sometimes pull the blade off the wheel. As soon as the blade touches any metal, it is ruined. Here I start with the breast cut and cut in to the stop-cut line.

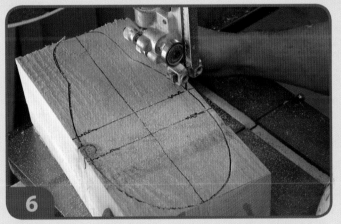

Cut the tail section up to the stop-cut line. Notice that the body will remain together and stay together for the side profile cutting.

Again, verify that the table is perpendicular; then, cut the side profile. Start by removing the lower rump section, beginning at the tail.

Cut the upper rump and tail area, making a stop cut below the primaries.

Make a perpendicular cut into the previous line, and then remove the small V of wood near the primaries. This will make a good, clean cut to elevate the primaries and give the decoy that traditional look.

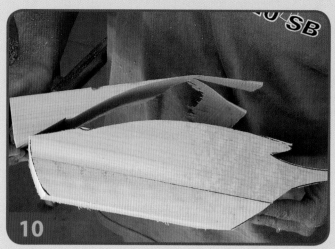

10

Now, starting at the primaries, make the cut all the way down the back and out through the neck region. Make sure that the area where the head attaches is smooth and level. (You can use a disc sander later in the project to clean up this area if it is not smooth.)

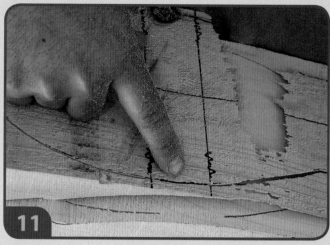

11

Notice that the stop-cut region held the side pieces on, providing stability when cutting out the decoy. Now, using the pattern, add the profile lines back on and cut off the sides.

12

Here is what the final cutout blank for this project should look like, using the pattern provided.

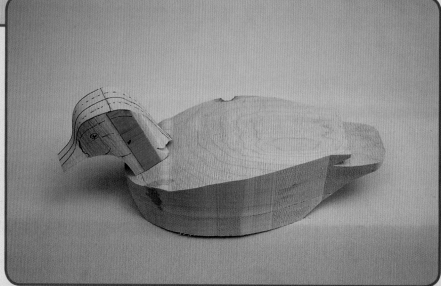

ROUGHING OUT THE DECOY

The lines that will guide you through roughing out the body are some of the most important lines that you will add to the decoy. I have the lines I want to rough cut to and the lines I want to leave as the high marks of the shoulders and side pocket. These lines will help you to maintain the overall flow and look of the decoy. It is my opinion that decoys today are too "lumpy bumpy" because of power tools. Using hand tools helps to make the birds more streamlined so they have that traditional look.

Throughout this book, I will provide alternative actions. There is more than one way to make a decoy, and I am just showing you one way that works for me. I like to have a procedure to follow so I do not feel lost, but I am always open to new ideas or techniques or alternative methods. That flexibility is why this hobby is so enjoyable. If you see a technique or tool that might adapt to your style, try to incorporate it into what you are making.

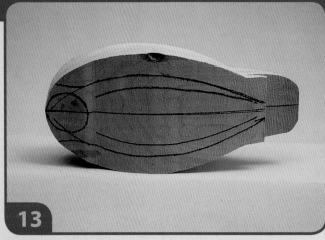

13

On the top view, I added the centerline and two sets of top lines. The inner set of guidelines is for the high mark; the outer set is where I will remove wood with the drawknife. Also mark the head location so that you are careful not to remove any wood in this area.

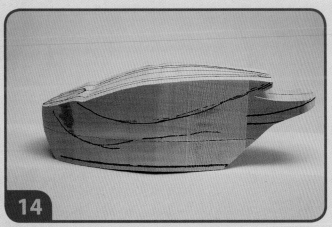

14

Here is the side profile. I added the thickness and location of the tail as well as the rounded bottom and wing profile. These lines guide me through the wood removal process. I take the wood from between the lines I drew on the top and these side lines.

MASTER TIP

Styling the Bottom of the Decoy
Knowing the different styles of decoys will help you decide how you want to carve your bird. In shaping the bottom of your decoy, there are two categories to understand: the Delaware-River-style decoy and the St.-Clair-Flats-style decoy. The Delaware River style has been a very respected and well-recognized style, perfected by John English and John Blair. This type of decoy has a rounded bottom, an incised tail, and V-cut primaries. It also floated well in rivers where rough water was less frequent. The St.-Clair-Flats-style decoy has a very flat bottom with a steeper chine on the sides. This style of decoy maintained its stability in rough water. The wood duck in this book falls somewhere between these two styles.

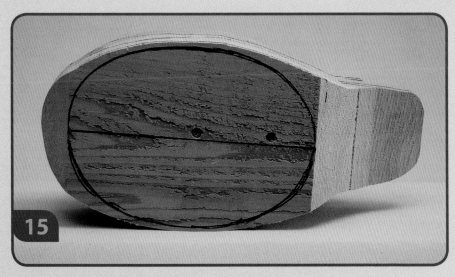

15

The bottom of the bird is a highly critical area, and I take my time deciding what to remove and how much of a flat area I am going to leave. I have found that each carver alters the amount of wood to be removed from the bottom of his decoy. Some like a round bottom and so would prefer a wider decoy with a steep chine (the angular intersection of the bottom and sides). I have selected something between a Delaware-River-style and a St.-Clair-Flats-style decoy. I believe that a wood duck will be in calmer waters than other ducks, so I want a flat bottom to make this bird light and move around in the slightest wind. I will add very little weight to him so that he is not too heavy to pack and take to the hunting area.

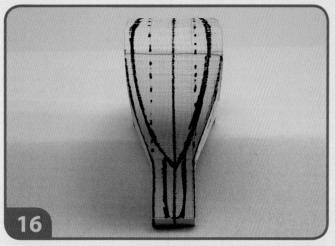

16

I add more lines to the head before I start removing wood with the knife. On top, I add the crown width and the rough dimensions. I also verify the width again. I make this a rough guess and then refine as I go, making sure the head is symmetrical.

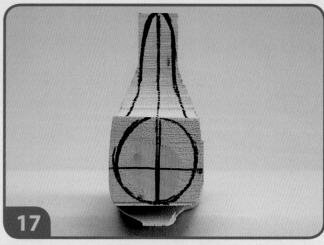

17

On the bottom of the head, I add a circle that aligns with the wide marks added in the previous step. I also transfer the top profile of the bill to the bottom of the blank. This mark gives me a rough-out size for the bill.

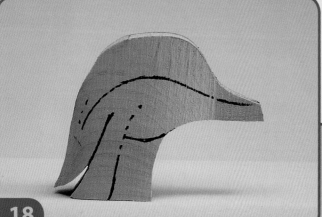

18

On the side profile, I add the eye trough and the widest area of the neck. From the top, I add the bill lines.

MASTER TIP

Using a Tupelo Knife

The one most important thing to learn with a tupelo knife is how to slice and shave the wood during the removal process. To cut with a tupelo knife, start your cuts at the heel of the knife (closest to the handle). Then, slide the cut toward the tip, using the whole blade to make the cut. Once you train yourself to do this, carving becomes less labor intensive.

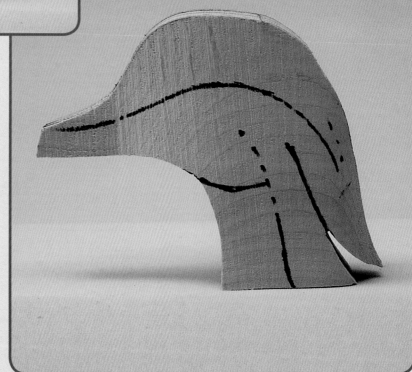

CARVING THE HEAD

On each and every decoy I make, I start off with the head. I like to get a feel for the bird, the face, and the attitude of the head so that the body matches. I believe that a good head can carry a so-so body, but a bad head can ruin a well-carved decoy body. So, I do spend more time on the head than most other carvers because I feel that I can create a lifelike bird in this area more than I can in the other regions. The bill and eyes are extremely important, and in future sections I will take a generous amount of time explaining these concepts.

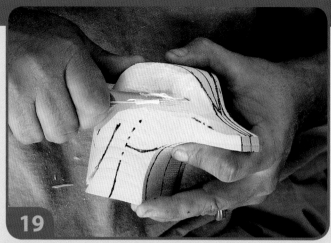

Starting with a knife I am comfortable with, I remove a large amount of wood. This is a step that is more craftsmanlike than artistic. From the eye-trough line, remove wood up to the top quarter line we drew on the top profile. Do this on both sides of the head and match them up.

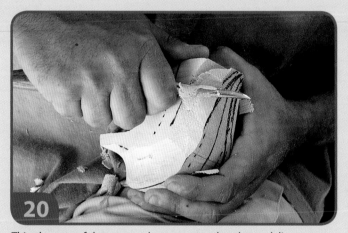

Thin the area of the crest and remove wood to the neck line.

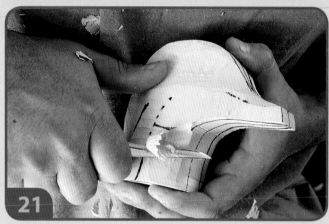

Start to remove wood in the neck. Continue to round and check for symmetry.

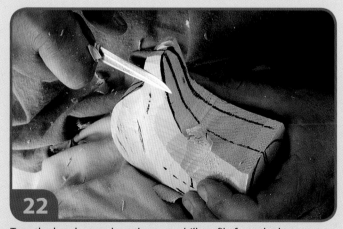

Turn the head up and cut the upper bill profile from the bottom, watching the lines you added.

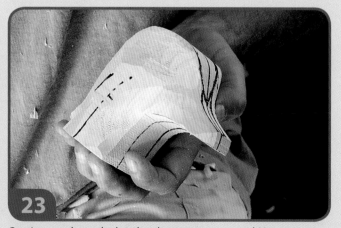

Continue to shape the head and remove more wood. You are not looking to reach the "final product" with a certain number of knife strokes. This can be a time-consuming process when you are new to the technique, but, once you get the hang of removing wood with a knife and use good cedar, you will find this step extremely enjoyable and relaxing. Now that the head is close enough and roughed out, we can start to bring the body down to size.

SHAPING THE BODY

For this part, you'll need to attach the mount to the bottom of the decoy and place the decoy on the work station. If you do not have this type of vise, try to fabricate a different approach to hold the bird. A large wood vise will work, or attach a wood block to the decoy body and place the wood block in a metal vise.

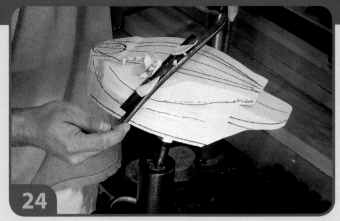

I mentally place a line across the midsection of the bird to indicate the grain line. It usually corresponds with the middle of the bird. On this decoy, the line is about two-thirds of the way back. I start to remove wood with a large, wide-bladed drawknife that acts like a plane. This wide blade will not allow deep chunks of wood to be removed during the rough-out process.

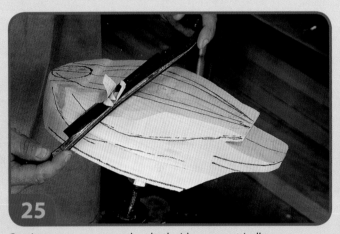

Continue to remove wood on both sides symmetrically.

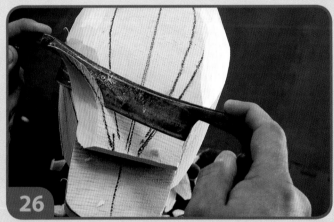

Now swing the bird around and start to remove wood toward the tail. Remember where the primaries are and where the wood will "chunk out." You will need to be careful because this area of the grain can pop off. Go slowly and remove smaller portions of wood. Because you are going with the grain, large pieces may cut away. Just be mindful of where your blade is as you cut.

Now that more wood has been removed, you'll need to make a strategic cut against the grain. Push in toward the grain on the upper rump area to remove the V-shaped section of wood. This maneuver is like a stop cut on a band saw.

Now come down on an angle to meet the stop cut and pop out that section of wood. Match the sides.

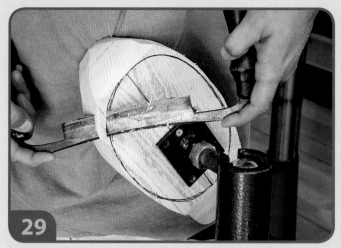

29

Shift the bird and start with the breast, removing wood between the two lines and continuously rounding the bird.

30

Again, shift the bird and start on the lower rump and undertail regions, taking the wood up to the line where the tail goes into the upper and lower rump areas.

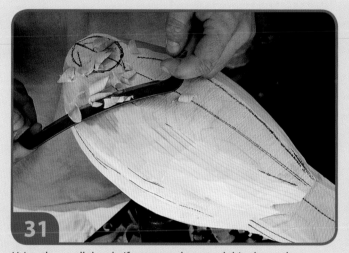

31

Using the small drawknife, start to shape and thin the neck area.

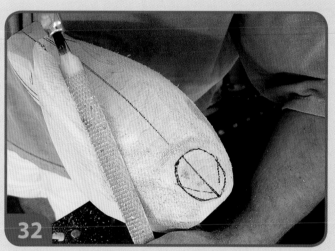

32

Start to round the whole body with long, rasping motions to shape the body.

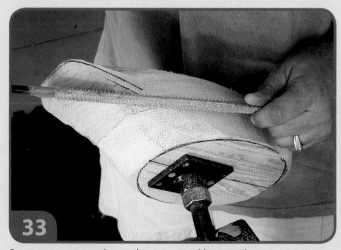

33

Remove more wood near the upper and lower tail areas.

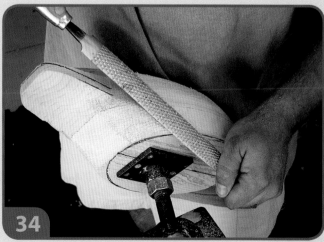

34

Now shape the lower tail area.

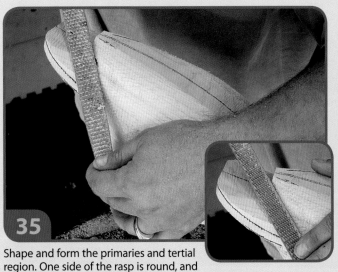

35

Shape and form the primaries and tertial region. One side of the rasp is round, and the other is flat. Use the rounded side for this task.

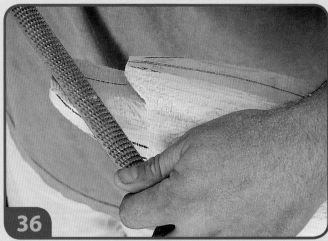

36

Shape and flatten out the upper tail region.

37

At this point, I select a spokeshave to smooth out the bird and remove any of the harsh lines or dips that I created with the rasp. I like the look of a spokeshaven bird, and I see no reason why you couldn't stop carving here, not sand the decoy, and just paint it.

MASTER TIP

Sanding Is Not a Requirement

I think some of the old-timers actually stopped after using a spokeshave and did not sand their decoys. To achieve an older look or a rougher-looking decoy, you can leave the bird in this texture, stress it with sunlight and water, and then paint it, creating a new and interesting look for a decoy. With the improvements in tools, technology, and paints, there are still hundreds of ideas carvers can come up with to make their own work look unique. I am sure that with some experimentation and creativity, one could come up with a super look for a true gunning decoy.

38

Shift the bird around and start to remove wood toward the neck. Be careful not to remove any wood near the connection point of the head with the spokeshave.

39

Flip the bird over and smooth out the bottom chine.

FORMING THE NECK

Now that the head and the body have been shaped separately, it is time to join them temporarily and form the neck and upper breast union. We'll be setting the head on the shelf area where it will attach and marking the location where it will be glued. You can make the area where the head attaches smooth and level, or you can leave it rough to enhance the mechanical bond of the two pieces of wood and make the chemical bond of the glue to the wood that much better. We'll also separate the two body sections, locate the area where the head will attach, and drill a pilot hole.

40

Place the head on the body where you want to secure it. Then, draw a circle around the neck. If the head sits evenly on the neck, mark the location of the screw. The screw should be on the centerline at a location to the carver's liking. Pre-drill through the top portion of the body so that, when you screw the head in place, you don't crack the neck. Use a 2" to 3" galvanized deck screw to hold the head in place.

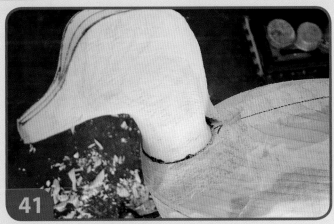

41

The head would not sit flush, so, after I marked it, I took a gouge and removed some of the cape area to make it sit on the body more evenly.

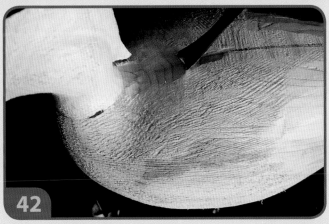

42

Once the head is attached, I can continue to shape the neck and breast area with the rasp and the knife. I use a large 8 mm rounded gouge to remove wood from the cape area.

43

In this photo, you see a better estimate of how much wood is removed.

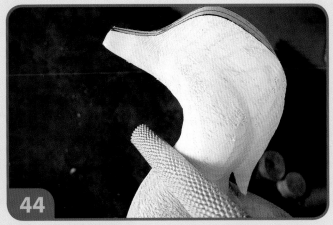

44

Shift to the neck. Using the flat part of the smaller rasp, smooth out the transition from the head to the neck.

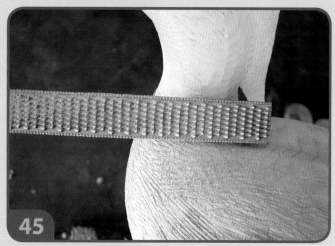

45

Using the other side of the rasp, round out the neck.

46

That same contour is near the upper rump area. Remove more wood there also.

47

I have included this photo to show the difference between the left side, which is rasped, and the right side, which is spokeshaved. The nice part about the rasped area is that the bird starts to get some feather flow. I personally like gunning birds with this roughness to them; they look more usable than when they are smooth. They also refract light better and give off a flatter finish when painted.

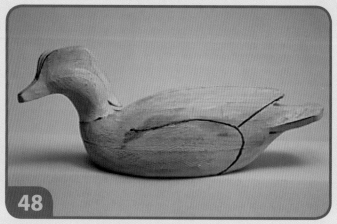

48

Now, refer to the pattern on pages 26 and 27 and draw the side pocket line from the side profile. Note that this is not the top view but the side view. This is a different S curve than the top line you will add in the next step.

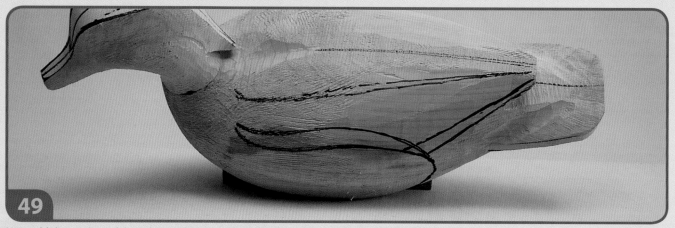

49

Now add the top line of the side pocket. This two-dimensional line actually meets at the front shoulder area and then on the top of the back side pocket. There are two lines drawn on the decoy now that indicate the position of the side pocket. The top view shows the side pocket's placement in relation to the width of the bird. The side view shows the shape of the side pocket. When the wood is removed, the union of these two lines will form a three-dimensional line that is the correct shape of the side pocket. This complex curve, part of "carving to the round," takes time to understand.

50

Wood will be removed from the blackened area.

MASTER TIP

Carving to the Round

The term "carving to the round" was first introduced to me by Richard LeMaster, and those words have remained with me ever since. Each time I start to rough out a bird, I remind myself that the bird should be round and that I must take it to that state from the beginning. All of the other detail you add is small and can be carved from within that rounded sculpture. This makes a great amount of sense when you are sculpting a bird. If you do not have Richard's book, I highly recommend going to a library and reading Chapter 12, pages 143 to 148. In a nutshell, the theory he presents is that from the center of the back to the waterline of the bird, there is a gentle arc that flows from that point, down to the edge of the side pocket where the water meets. He also advocates the idea that nothing in nature has straight lines; everything is rounds and curves. So, as an artist, it is extremely important to incorporate that in your creation.

Book information:

Wildlife in Wood by Richard LeMaster

Published in 1978 by Contemporary Books, Inc.

Library of Congress Control Number: 77-071565

ISBN 0-9601-84015

51

From the back of the bird, you can see the area of wood that needs to be removed. Add the line on the opposite side and level out. Remove wood from the show side of the bird first, and then match the sides.

52

Using a large 90-degree V-gouge, I start in the middle of the bird (grain line) and then begin to take out the blackened area. Go slowly.

53

Continue pushing toward the tail and remove about half of the total depth of ⅜". Do not try to remove all of the wood with one long push or you risk removing too much wood.

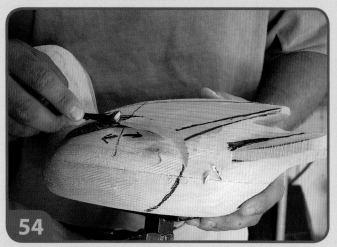

54

Push all of the way to the middle of the back end of the side pocket, halfway to the correct depth of approximately ½".

55

Loosen the vise and turn the bird around. Starting at the midpoint of the area, push through with the palm gouge to remove the blackened area.

56

Continue to remove more wood on the front of the side pocket.

MASTER TIP

Determining the Show Side
The show side of a bird is the side that viewers and judges would see when the bird is on display. Because the head of a decoy is usually turned, the side that allows the viewer to see more of the head is chosen as the show side. With that said, be sure that all of the feather groups flow smoothly on that side of the bird!

DEFINING THE PRIMARIES

An important part of any decoy is the flight feathers, or primaries. Puddle ducks usually carry their primaries at a higher angle and up away from the upper rump area, elevated from their bodies more than the diver ducks, who carry theirs closer to their bodies. The angle at which you place the primaries will be critical to the pose of this bird. With a swimming posture, they should look sleek and out of the way so that this bird can dart around the marsh looking for food and remain alert. In addition, lifting the primaries will showcase your carving talents. I will also remind you that lifting them or undercutting them too much may make them too fragile, so there is a fine line regarding how much wood you remove. On this style of decoy, less is more.

57

Now that the side pocket is established, let's define the primaries. Start at the intersection where the wing comes up and out of the side pocket. Push the V-gouge down into the wood and remove the line that was drawn in. This puts a nice clean step between the upper rump and the primaries.

MASTER TIP

Carving the Primaries
Here's one way that the carvers of the Delaware River style put in the primaries. First, draw the primaries in a balanced V. Then, remove wood with a large parting gouge. This technique is very simple with the proper tool.

58

Remove more wood and set the rump height to the correct dimension.

59

Shift to the wide fishtail gouge and start to round and clean up the deep cuts. This gouge has a slight bend, and I sometimes use it upside down to take off wood. The gentle bend in the gouge provides a good radius. Again, using the largest tool for the job is a rule of thumb. On larger birds, I use a fishtail gouge that is 3" wide.

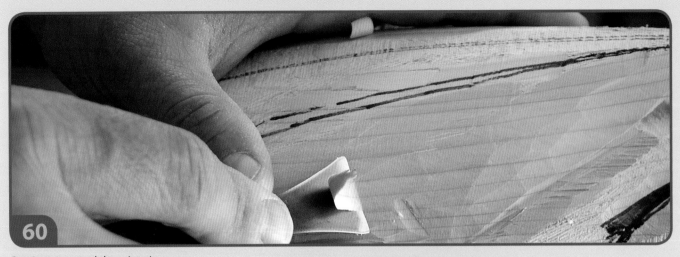

60

Continue to round the primaries.

61

Alternating between the V-gouge and the fishtail gouge, continue to round the same area.

MASTER TIP

Tool Techniques

Notice that I am using the fishtail gouge upside down. Using the gouge upside down will minimize the amount of bite the tool has into the wood and allows the carver to almost sand the wood. Basically, this technique planes the wood, detailing it without tearing it, and provides a smooth surface.

SHAPING THE HEAD

Now that we have set the primaries and the side pocket, disassemble the bird and remove the head from the body. The next step is to shape the head, insert the eye, and finish the bill.

When shaping, you must prepare the head with strategically placed lines, showing where to remove wood and where the next steps are. These lines help to minimize that "lost" feeling carvers sometimes get when they don't know exactly what to do next. In this section, I will also provide some rough measurements for the head, but beware—you will be required to adjust to your carving. The idea here is to get within a ballpark area. The most important thing is to capture the look of a wood duck.

Now that the head has been removed, we are ready to take the head down to its final size and shape.

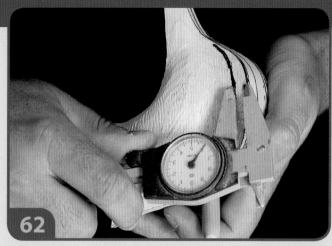

Draw about a 6 mm edge to the crown on the side profile.

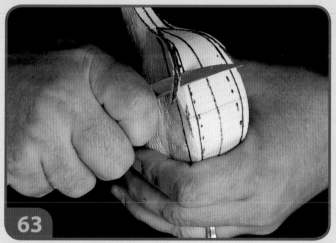

Add the same 6 mm edge to the crown on the top profile. These lines will help to align the symmetry of the head. Select your favorite knife and start to remove wood on a 45-degree angle between the two lines we just added to the head.

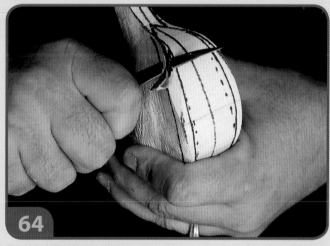

Start at the middle grain point on the widest part of the head and remove the wood forward.

Here is a front view of the wood removal.

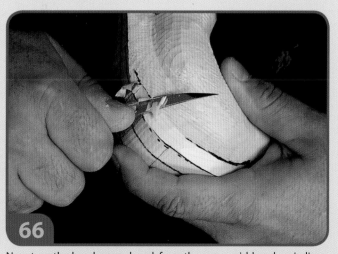

Now turn the head around, and, from the same mid-head grain line, start to remove wood across the crown, then down the crest.

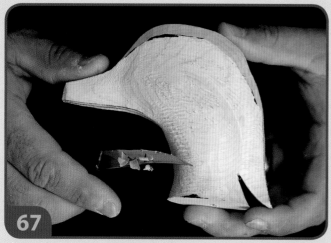

67

Here is where you should be with wood removal. We are attempting to remove wood in a systematic method to achieve a rounded look.

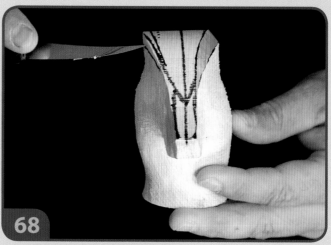

68

Now remove wood from the opposite side. Both sides should match.

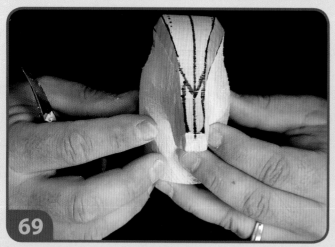

69

I am starting to round over the head. Work back and forth between both sides so that wood is removed symmetrically.

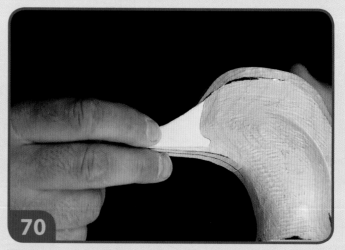

70

We are now ready to locate the bill. Using the pattern, trace the bill, cut it out, and use it as a template for the head. Place the template on the bill at the end of the cutoff, and draw the line between the face and the bill. This line is known as the basal line.

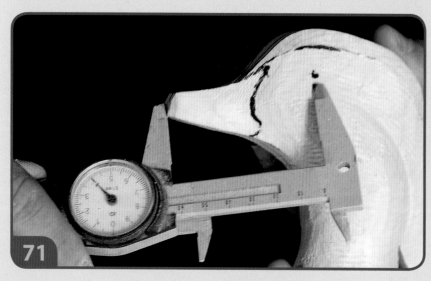

71

Draw the basal line on the side profile. Add it to the other side and make sure that both lines are symmetrical. If they are not symmetrical, sand and redo them. Now, using the pattern, place the eye on the side profile. The location of the eye is about 67 mm from the tip of the bill. I find that I set the distance on the show side of the bird and then match the back side to the show side.

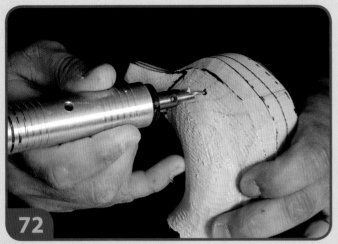

72

There are a number of ways to drill the eye into the side profile (see an alternate method on page 50). You may not even choose to insert an eye. You might choose to carve the eye, use a tack, or burn the eye (see pages 51 and 52 for information on carving a wooden eye). Whichever way you decide, just make sure that the eyes are level and not too exposed. Don't be afraid to set the eyes into the holes. Bug eyes make the birds look weird and not lifelike. In this photo, I am drilling holes with a 10 mm drill.

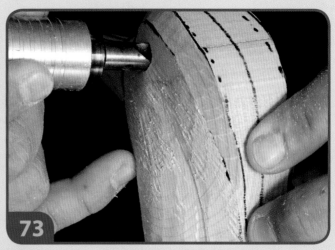

73

Drill the hole at a perpendicular angle to the eye socket.

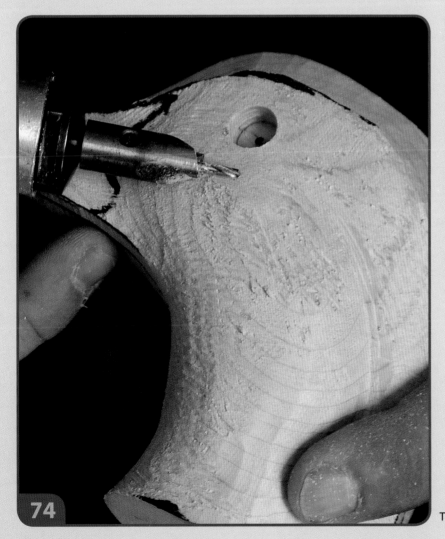

74

MASTER TIP

Shaping the Eyes
When inserting the eyes, do not make them look too modern. Old masters kept their eyes more surface mounted, with no shaping for the eye. These older eyes also appeared round. Modern carvers, in contrast, sink the eyes deeper and shape the eye into an almond shape. The eyes play an important part in making the decoy look older and will enhance the bird's age.

The hole is 5 mm deep.

ALTERNATIVE METHOD FOR ADDING AN EYE SOCKET TO INSERT A GLASS EYE

I took three different sizes of brass tubing, about 4" long, and glued them to dowels, which will act like handles. Then, I sharpened the end of the brass tube so that it will cut when pressure is applied and the tube is twisted into the cedar. Because cedar is very soft, the tube makes a nice, clean cut in which to set the glass eye.

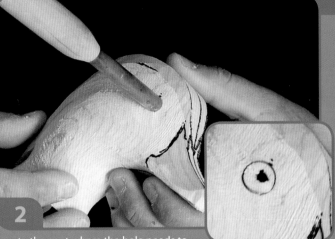

Locate the spot where the hole needs to be, and align the "eyeholer" on the head. With a good amount of force, press and twist the brass tube into the head about 5 or 6 mm. Remove the tube, and you will have a perfectly round hole.

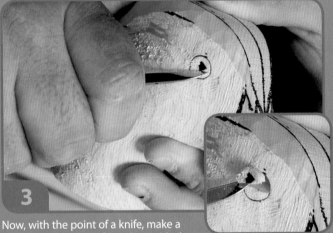

Now, with the point of a knife, make a cut within that circle from the 3 o'clock position to the 9 o'clock position. Do not go past the edge of the circle.

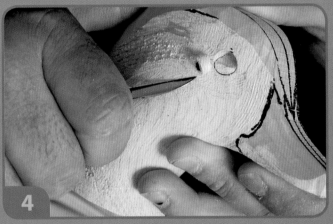

The piece will pop right out.

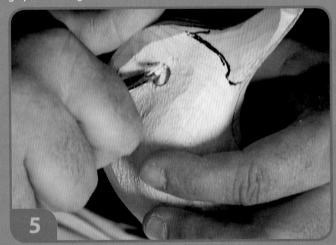

Now make two more cuts to remove what wood is left. Go slowly. The other half will pop right out like the first one did. You might also try practicing this procedure on a separate piece of wood before you attempt it on the head.

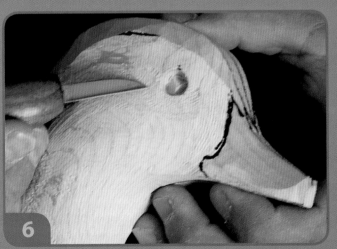

Here is what the eye should look like when done manually without electricity.

CARVING A WOODEN EYE

One way to make a decoy look even older or more authentic is to carve a wooden eye. Today there are some shorebird carvers who carve the eye right in and then paint it to make it look like a realistic eye, and they do pretty well with that approach. After a few practice attempts, I am positive that you, too, will be able to do the same. Here is a quick example of how to add a wooden eye.

Using a brass tube sharpened at one end (see page 50), score a circle where the eye should be located on the head. The diameter of the tube should match the size of the eye. For this exercise, I am demonstrating on a scrap piece of wood.

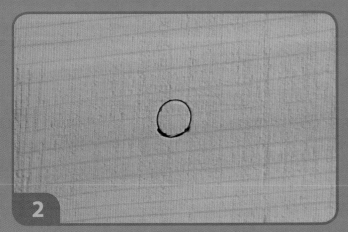

Here you can see the scored circle in the wood.

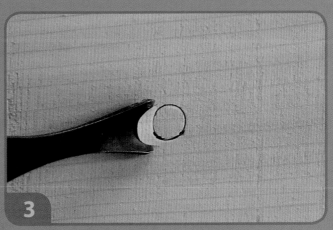

With a wide gouge, remove the front part of the eye, being mindful not to push too far. You can easily take the eye right off if you slip and push too far.

Shift to the back of the eye and push out the back.

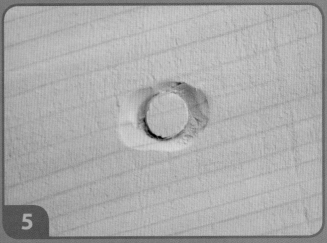

Shift the gouge around the eye, using the edge of the gouge to remove the wood all around the circle. The cleaner you make the cuts, the less sanding you will have to do.

CARVING A WOODEN EYE (CONTINUED)

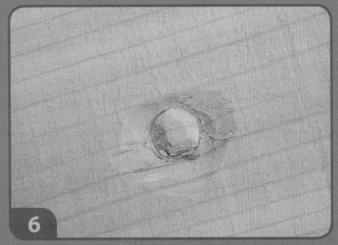

6 Using the tip of a sharp-pointed knife, round off the circle.

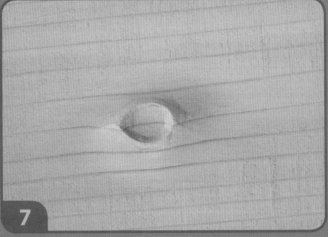

7 Finger sand with 120-grit then 180-grit sandpaper.

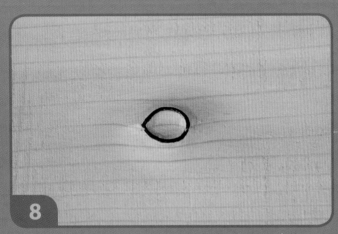

8 Use a ballpoint pen to burnish an edge around the eye. This will create a smooth ring around the eye.

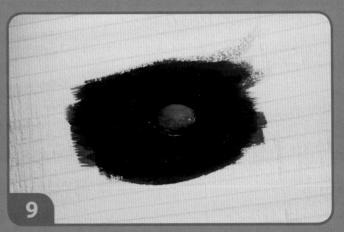

9 Paint green around the eye. Paint the eye red. This is the first coat.

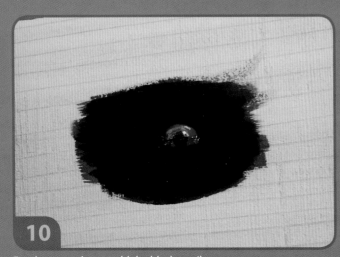

10 For the second coat, add the black pupil.

11 The third coat consists of a small white dot to the top back of the pupil as a highlight. Add a gloss coat as the final coat, and you have a wooden eye.

SHAPING THE BILL AND HEAD

As with any decoy, the head and bill make up the "look" of the bird that you are trying to create. What you need to keep in mind with this project is that you are trying to capture the essence and shape of the bill without all of the extra detail. Each species' bill has evolved to suit that species' feeding habits. This bill's design helps the wood duck effectively feed on its specific type of food. What you will want to do is make sure that you position the bill onto the face of the bird and carve it at the correct angle; these are two of the most important aspects. If these two attributes are carved wrong, no amount of carved or painted detail will make up for these errors. It is vital that the overall detail of shape and the position are correct.

On some decoys I produce, I omit the nostril because it has been said that this inserts a weak area on the bill. I also try to minimize how thin and sharp areas are on the bill because these will make it fragile and are places that will wear down easily. Reviewing old birds in personal collections and public museums or in the gallery of this book will provide great reference material for this area.

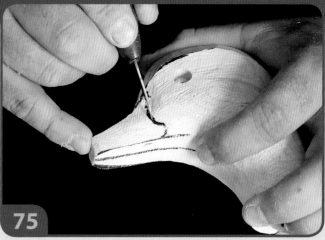

Now it's time to shape the bill. Using a short-bladed detail knife, start at the lower portion of the basal line and cut up to the top near the culmen into that line. Do not go too deep; if you cut too deep, the cut will look hacked out. Try to remove just a small amount of wood and make these cuts extremely precise.

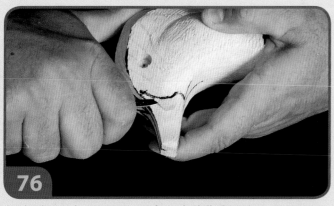

Cut back into that previous cut from the bill. This is known as a stop cut. Be careful—you are cutting into the grain, and a large chip may pop out unexpectedly.

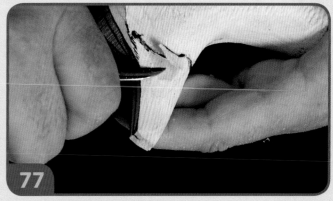

This is the amount of wood that should come out.

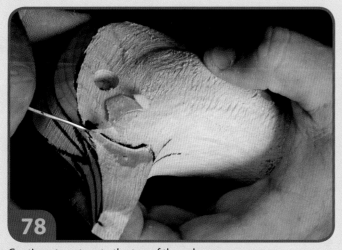

Continue to cut up to the top of the culmen.

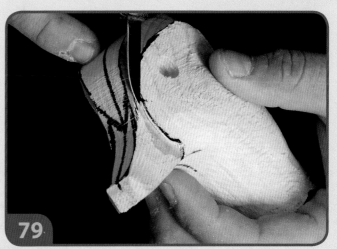

Clean up the top cut and take out more wood.

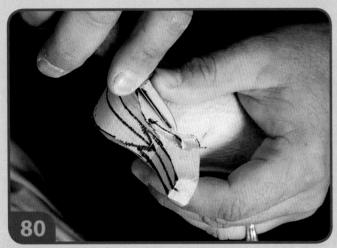

80

We have removed the wood on the bill; now we have to bevel the face into the bill. Remove the hard edge that was created by taking away wood from the bill area.

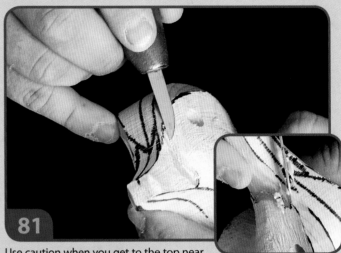

81

Use caution when you get to the top near the culmen; make sure you do not chip off the top portion of the bill. Do not try to remove this wood all in one cut. To remove the section of wood, it may take a number of passes, progressively pushing harder and harder to make the cuts match.

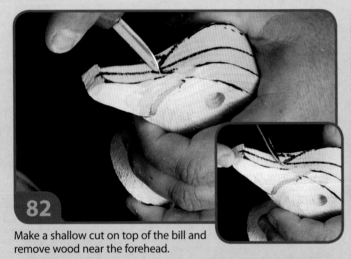

82

Make a shallow cut on top of the bill and remove wood near the forehead.

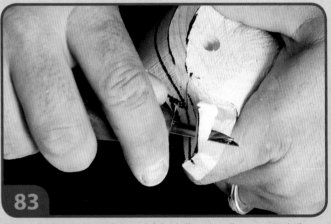

83

Shape the bill. Start at the top of the bill and scallop out the bill.

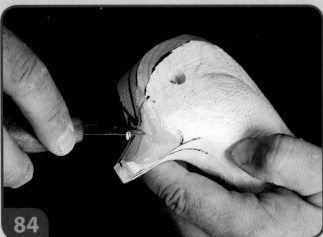

84

Keep shaping the bill, matching both sides of the bill to each other.

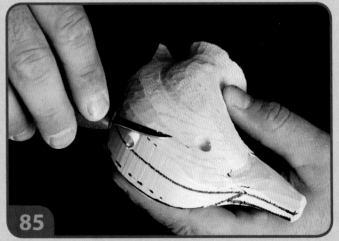

85

Continue rounding and shaping the top of the crown. Now take off the black line. I call this "chasing wood"; I use the small chip marks on the head to draw lines and then work down the side. Chasing wood can be better explained as systematically removing wood by looking at the previous mark left by the knife. While carving, I look at these lines and strategically place my knife between that mark and the next one I will make so that the wood is not just hacked away but has a smoother transition.

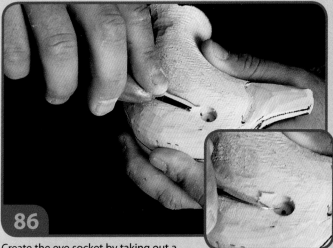

86

Create the eye socket by taking out a series of small cuts near the eyes. Start at the back of the eye and cut out a small V. This will be sanded and smoothed out later.

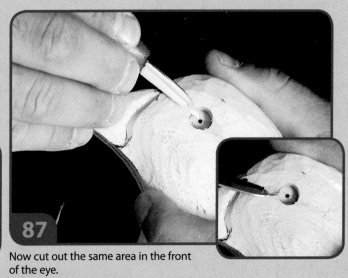

87

Now cut out the same area in the front of the eye.

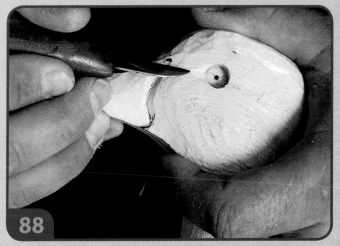

88

The grooves in front of and behind the eye are completed.

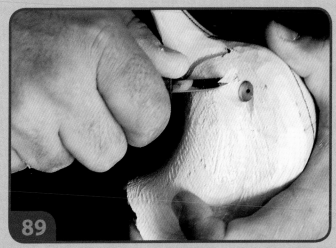

89

Remove more wood under the eye.

90

Here is the head and bill after they have been carved with a knife. Some carvers leave the birds like this, then lightly sand and paint them. I like to feel the head come alive by using a knife. The knife smoothes out the head, and the wood is not torn off with a rasp or a power tool.

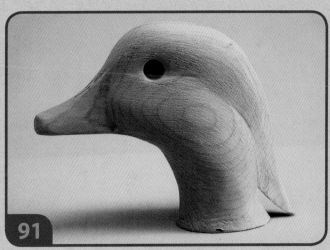

91

The opposite side has been sanded with 60-grit sandpaper.

All waterfowl have two mandibles, the upper and the lower mandible. To show this small indent is critical, and yet not too much wood should be removed to prevent this area from becoming fragile. I recommend that you practice on a spare piece of wood or a separate head. This will be a precise cut, and very little sanding will occur. The cut will also add some attitude to the bird's look. Again, I recommend that you evaluate past masters and see how they accomplished this area; then, modify your own approach between what you see and what you like.

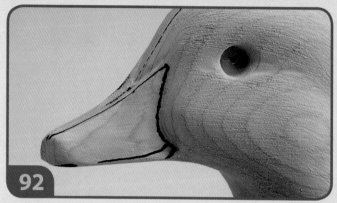

Sand the bill with 120-grit sandpaper before cutting the lower mandible.

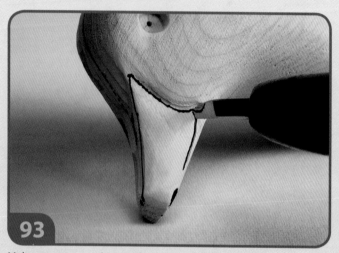

Make a stop cut, sinking in the tip of the knife near the lower mandible intersection.

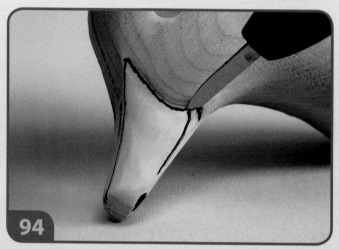

Now set the knife's tip in the opposite direction and cut along the face.

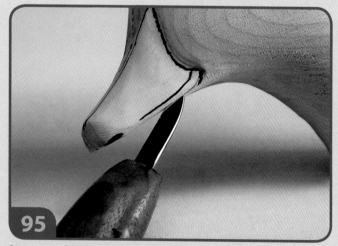

Starting at the exit point of the previous cut, make a long cut that angles up into the first cut. Removing this sliver of wood will separate the upper and lower mandibles.

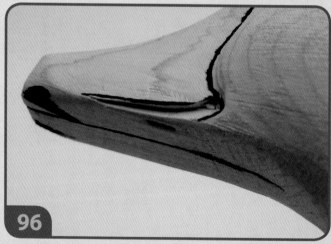

An example of what the cut looks like is shown in this photo.

97 Remove wood under the nail.

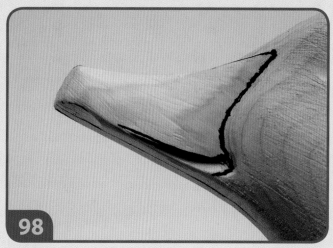

98 A side view shows the wood that was removed.

99 The head has been sanded again with 80-grit sandpaper and is ready for the eyes. Adding more bill detail, such as the nostril and the nail, is really a matter of personal taste and style. I add them to the bill and slightly thin the bill based on my own preferences, but be sure to experiment and find what works best for you.

EYE SELECTION AND EYE INSERTION

A variety of eyes are available for this decoy, so eye selection will be a personal choice. If you add a blended eye, a multicolored glass eye, the decoy will look newer and less antique. A tack or a carved eye will look more appropriate. Even though they look newer, I prefer to add glass eyes to my decoys. Some glass eyes look older than others, and the older-looking ones are what I use. I highly suggest that you try different eye selections. Find the look you like, and then perfect that look.

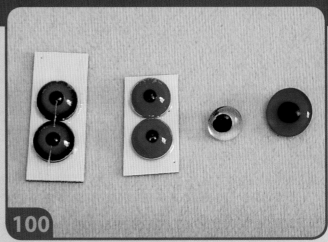

Here are four varieties of glass decoy eyes. Left to right: blended, plain red, clear (which you have to paint yourself), and flat-colored eyes. I chose the blended eye.

I use cream-colored Apoxie Sculpt, a brand of two-part epoxy, to set my eyes.

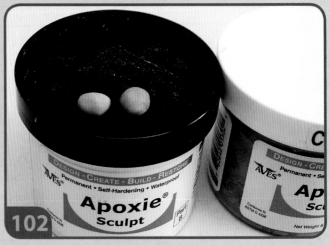

Remove two large peas of equal size, one from each container, and mix them together thoroughly.

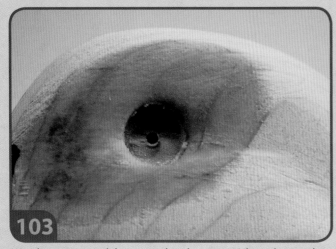

Wet the area around the eye so that the putty sticks to the wood.

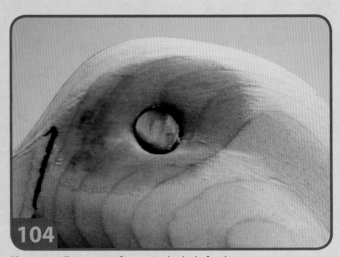

Place a small amount of putty in the hole for the eye.

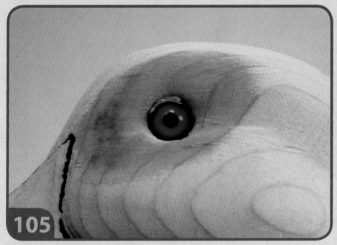

105

Set the eye into the putty and use the eraser end of a pencil to push in the eye to the correct depth. It allows you to tilt and push the eye as required.

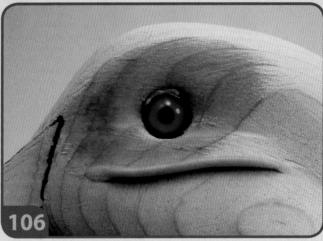

106

With the remaining putty, roll a small line about twice the thickness of pencil lead. This rope of material will be used around the eye.

107

Set the putty rope around the eye. Then, wet the putty and push it into place around the eye.

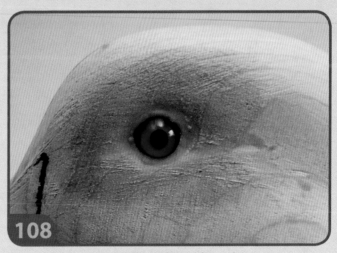

108

Dip your finger in warm water and smooth out the putty.

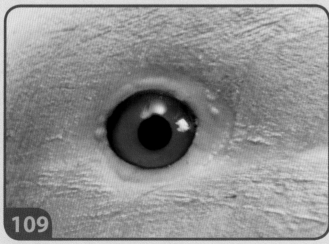

109

The eye is set. Allow the epoxy to dry according to the manufacturer's directions. Repeat the steps for the other eye.

There are several reasons why one would hollow the decoy's body. I believe all are very legitimate reasons, so I do this to all of my decoys. If a bird is left solid, over time the bird will check and crack, opening up the decoy to allow moisture and humidity to seep into the bird, whether it is on the mantle or ready for the rig. Once you hollow the bird, it will accomplish equilibrium of the temperature inside the bird and the ambient room temperature, reducing any chance that the bird will split open and crack. Hollowing will also allow the removal of that inner core of wood that may be wet with moisture not able to escape, again cracking and checking the decoy. The other issue is that, during actual use, a hollowed decoy lightens the load a hunter needs to carry, and the bird floats better, providing more action and lifelike motion. Finally, it is also a neat conversation starter to say that you hollow out your decoys. Most new collectors or long-time admirers will be in awe of your ability.

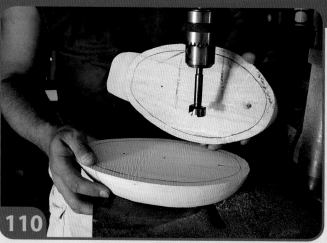

110

Separate the body parts. Using a pencil, make a line 10 mm in from the edge of the top and bottom parts of the body. Keep in mind that the neck and the tail areas are areas of concern. Be careful when removing wood from these parts.

111

Set the depth of your drill press so that there will be about ½" of wood remaining after the bird has been hollowed out.

112

Start to hollow out the top section. I make a clean cut where the screw for the head will go. Continue removing wood with a Forstner bit. Using a bit is quicker than using a gouge.

113

Here is the hollowed-out bottom section.

114

Complete the hollowing process for the top and bottom parts of the decoy.

ASSEMBLY

Now glue the decoy together. I use West System two-part epoxy. This is boat-building glue, and it is very strong and durable. You can find it online or in many boating supply stores. If the decoy is not going to go in the water, use Devcon five-minute epoxy. If you plan to hunt over the bird, I suggest that you use an epoxy with a longer drying period; these are usually waterproof.

Add registration marks to help you align the head. Then, place glue between the head and the upper body section. Align the head and tighten the screw. Next, place liberal amounts of glue around the lower body section. Clamp the top and bottom sections together, holding them in place. I drape two large bags of lead material that weigh about 40 pounds each over the bird to set the glue. Then, I clean up the shop. When the glue is dry (after approximately four hours), I hand sand the two joints smooth with 80-grit sandpaper. If you want to make the decoy look even older, try removing some glue in the joint.

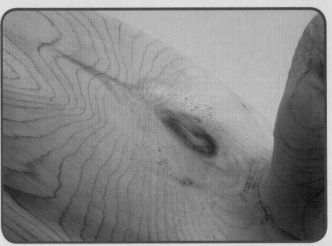

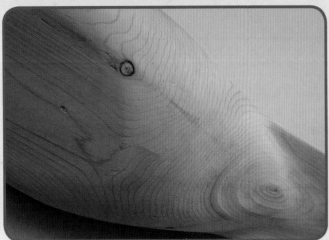

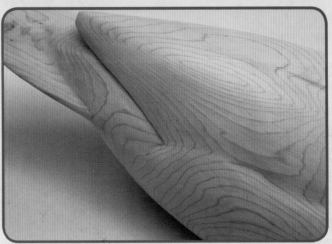

Note: Before we move on to stressing and aging the wood, it is a good idea to draw the pattern lines on the bird. These lines will also aid you in the initial phases of painting.

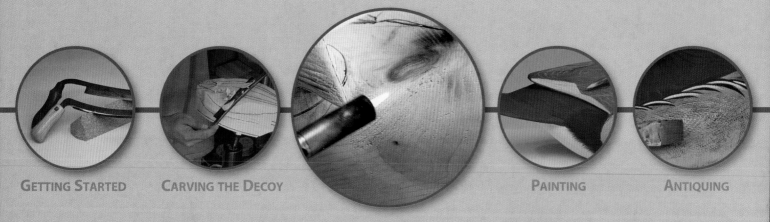

GETTING STARTED   CARVING THE DECOY   PAINTING   ANTIQUING

AGING THE WOOD

When making an antique decoy, the surface preparation for the decoy is paramount. Your understanding of the wood and the next series of steps you perform before you apply paint to the decoy are of the utmost importance. It is also extremely important that you experiment with this procedure and take notes. In this chapter, I'll show you a few techniques that I've learned over time. I highly recommend that you talk to as many other carvers as you can about the process. Be open to new ideas, too.

As you experiment with your own decoys, take good notes on what you do on each and every decoy. Take a different approach to different areas. For example, the bottom of the decoy may get one approach, while the head of the same decoy gets a different series of applications. Then, two or three weeks later, or maybe even a few months later, inspect the surface and see what it looks like. This will be your best source of information. Unless you actually get out there and do it, you will never know how some of these techniques can be incorporated into your own work.

Also note that different species of wood and each individual piece will react differently because of age, moisture content, region of harvest, humidity, and paint type, just to name a few factors. Again, experiment to find what works best for you.

A Tough Approach
The next set of instructions might be a bit difficult to perform. Now that you have sanded your decoy and have taken a good number of hours to create the decoy, you will have to ding and dent it up, as well as add heat and water to it—prior to even painting it.

There are many more ways to prepare the decoy's surface than what I have included here. The sky is the limit. I know some carvers who take more time with this step than they do with painting the bird. One carver in particular admits that it has taken him ten-plus years of learning to know how to make the wood look old. My goal is to make the bird look old and slightly beat up, as if it were used for 15 or 20 years.

The decoy that you are creating is your decoy. It is up to you to create the effects on the decoy that you want. You might carry the decoy around in the back of your truck for a month, leaving it out so it is exposed to the elements. Or you may choose to bury the decoy for a month underground. Again, there are many ways to make the wood look aged. It's up to you to find out what works best for you.

I know the first time I tried this I was extremely hesitant. With each decoy, this part gets easier and easier. So let's get started.

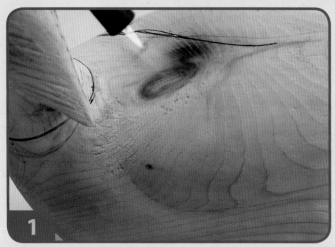

Evaluate your decoy. Look at the characteristics of the wood and locate the narrow grain lines, imperfections, or knots. On my decoy, a few knots were revealed through carving. To pop and crack them a little more than what they are, take a propane torch and, on low heat, apply some heat to them to open up the end grain and even create some cracks. Here I add some low heat to the knot in the cape area.

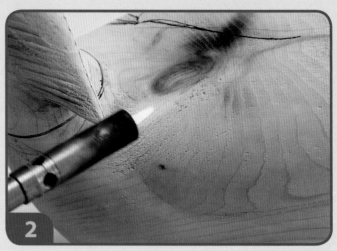

Change the angle at which you apply the heat, hitting the knot and beyond the grain to enhance the look of the area.

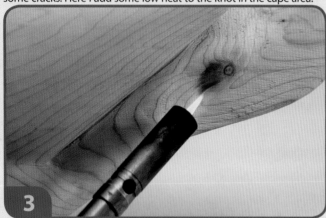

There was a small pin knot in the upper tail area; I applied a small amount of heat to it so that it would stand out.

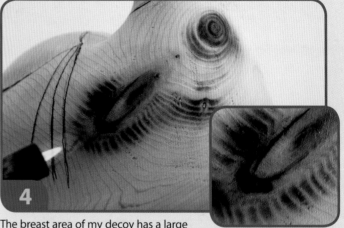

The breast area of my decoy has a large knot and a bird's-eye from the center of the tree. When heat is applied to the heartwood, you will get minute cracking that really adds years to the decoy. I applied heat to both areas. If you apply heat, be careful not to apply too much in any area that is close to the head joint. Too much heat will weaken the joint.

The crest of the wood duck can be enhanced as well. I used a small hand rasp to add feather flow. There are many other species of ducks that this effect will look good on, too.

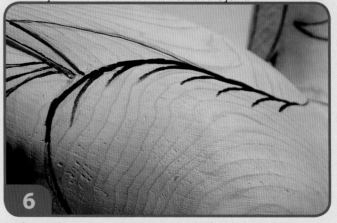

Further evaluation revealed that the back of the side pocket contains grain lines that look like feathers. I added heat to this area to bring out the grain even more.

7

Here is the decoy with heat added and then cleaned out with 00 steel wool.

8

Now, this may be the most difficult part of the project. Take the bird to a gravel driveway and drop the bird on the gravel a few times. This will put irregular patterns on the bird that you cannot reproduce. Be sure to drop it from a short height and only on its bottom or its sides; dropping the bird from a long distance or on its head could crack the neck. You may opt to omit this step if you want. However, I like the small dings and dents this procedure provides.

9

For smoother dents, I drop a chain on the bird, which will simulate a different dent than those made by the rocks.

10

The decoy now has the imperfections on it to my liking.

AGING MATERIALS AND EFFECTS

This list of wood-aging techniques will provide you with a quick reference and help get you started in your own techniques. My list continues to grow with each experiment and project I conduct. I recommend that you keep a list of your own so that, when the time comes to make another decoy, you have it handy and know what the outcome will most likely be. The most enjoyable part of this journey is when you discover a characteristic that appears by accident and it looks great. The options available certainly provide a wide-open palette for a creative mind.

Aging material	Application	Effect
River rock (collection of various rounded rocks from western riverbeds)	Drop on decoy from short height	Creates uneven dents and imperfections
Chain	Drop onto decoy from various heights and on different areas	Creates rounded, smooth dents
Propane grill	Burn decoy with flame in selected spots	Gives bird age and darkness
Rasp	Use on select places	Accentuates feather flow
Steel wool	Rub decoy after burning	Cleans out cracks and knots
Gravel	Drop decoy onto gravel	Creates small, irregular dents

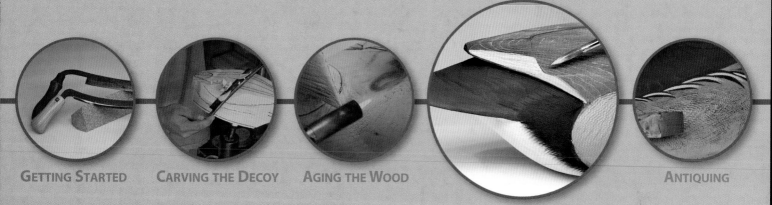

CHAPTER 4

GETTING STARTED   CARVING THE DECOY   AGING THE WOOD   ANTIQUING

PAINTING

I have always commented to new carvers that take a class, "Anyone can carve the decoy; not everyone can paint the decoy." And that is something I have witnessed for many years. Painting the decoy is the most important part of the decoy as far as I am concerned. After I am long gone, I want my waterfowl creations to tell a story that I was more of an artist than a craftsperson and that I spent more time with a brush in hand than I did with a blade. Painting a decoy will require some time and effort, patience, and practice. Various techniques will not come to you overnight, so do not give up on your first bird. You will learn many techniques in this chapter; some will come to you quickly, and

some will take a few more birds to learn. With this style of decoy, you can go extremely simple or very advanced and still have a beautiful bird when yours is complete. One aspect to remember is that, even though you are putting dents, dings, and scratches into this decoy, you should not think that a poor paint job is going to be okay. The decoy will always reflect that initial paint job, and what goes on top of it, what is removed from it, and how it is aged will directly affect the overall look of the finished product. Too many people think they can get away with a simple, easy paint job and the aging will cover it up, but that is not the case.

Selecting your paints

There are differences between oil and acrylic paints in regard to how they hold up and how they will react over time. A whole chapter could be devoted to this discussion, but the choice really depends on what the artist's personal preference is, what is available, and what finish the artist wants to achieve.

I prefer to use JansenArt acrylics (see **Figure 4.1**) due to the high-quality pigment that the company uses in its paints and the ASTM (American Society of Testing and Materials) safety standards. JansenArt paints are safe paints; they do not use harmful chemicals in them. Some other paints on the market do contain harmful chemicals and are not safe. For instance, brands with a color called "cadmium red" contain cadmium, a harmful chemical. I also do not care for the smell of oil thinners, and I'd rather not work with the rags and dangerous cleaning solvents required when using oils. **Note:** I have used the correct name for the corresponding color so that if you do choose to use oils, you will still be able to follow this procedure (see the chart on page 72).

Figure 4.1. A few of the paints used to paint the wood duck drake.

Painting techniques

Now—trust me on this—there is a learning curve here, and you should really try out the painting techniques in this book on a spare piece of wood before you try them on your decoy. Of course, there are many ways to paint, so feel free to experiment and use the methods that work best for you. The method I will show you in the following sections is one that has been proven reliable over time.

Prepare the paints. While some decoys require paint to be translucent, this style of decoy painting uses the paint straight out of the bottle with just a little water as thinner. This will increase the adhesion power of the paint because the binder in the paint is not thinned with as much water. A small amount of extender added to the paints will increase the open time of the paints, or the time during which the paints can be blended. Extender, however, will not affect the power of the paint.

By adding a small amount of water and some extender to the acrylics, you will get a nice, warm-butter-like consistency and an effective blending time. **Note:** When adding extender, do not use more than 20% extender to the amount of paint you have on your palette.

Study your materials. Prior to painting this decoy, think about the concept and design of hard lines and soft lines. Ducks and decoys have areas that stand out and pop. Those areas differ from bird to bird, so we, as carvers and painters, need to determine these areas at the beginning of the project. By looking at these areas before we paint, we know where to blend and where to start and stop each feather grouping. We will then come back and add the hard lines during follow-up steps.

Blending a hard line or hardening a soft line will be your decision based on your perception of the species. Of course, you want to keep the viewer's perceptions in mind, too, and always consult your reference material. So, while there is artistic license, you still need to be within some boundaries to make your decoy close to lifelike. When you push artistic license to beyond what the real, live duck shows you, then you automatically set off a flag for incorrectness.

For example, a blended soft area is the tail and upper tail coverts, but the feather edges of the tail are hard. The tertials are all blended, but a leading edge of white can be added later with a script brush. The whole side pocket is a blend, but the top edge of the side pocket is black-white-black with a certain proportion of color, and, if blended, it will look different than the reference photos. Look at the rest of the bird and try to determine those areas. We'll touch on this concept again as we go through the painting demonstration.

The order of painting. I paint my decoys from tail to bill, in that order. This order should become standard practice on each decoy you paint. Because a bird's feathers generally flow front to back (the front feather groups overlapping the next sections back), you can overlap an area in the previous section and clean up the feathers.

Blending. My personal style of painting involves blending colors directly on the decoy and not on the palette. I encourage you to give this method a try, but you can also use your palette for blending. We will also be doing some wet-on-wet blending, which we will cover specifically for each section. I will explain my methods and show you the brushes that I use, but you are more than welcome to change the brush based on your working style.

The goal is to find a technique that allows you to make a soft, clean blend. Paint swatches for the different sections have been provided as a reference against which you can check your finished areas.

Glazing. When the layer of paint you added comes out the way you want it to, put a clear matte coating (glaze) over the painted detail, locking it in place. Then, subsequent layers of paint will not affect the other layers underneath that glaze coat. A general rule of thumb is "if you like it, glaze it."

Painting tools

You will need a variety of brushes, including flats, rounds, and blenders. For blending areas, I use a fan blender and a mop to stipple. I also recommend that you have a clean, lint-free towel handy. You will be using the towel to dry off your blending brushes. The following list addresses the basic supplies I use and what their functions are.

Mediums: I use three basic mediums (see **Figure 4.2**) while I'm painting or when I'm preparing to paint: extender; glazing medium, which can be tinted and thinned 60% water to 40% glaze for an airbrush medium; and multi-surface sealer, which can be used to seal wood and cork prior to painting.

Figure 4.2. Extender, glazing medium, and multi-surface sealer are three mediums that are very useful for painting your decoy.

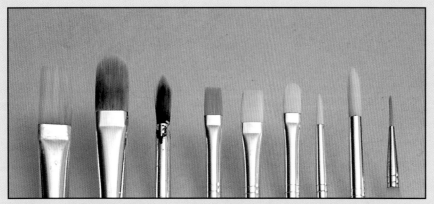

Figure 4.3. Inexpensive brushes are used to base coat the bird and are made of synthetic nylon. Pictured from left to right are a #6 flat, a #6 oval/cat's tongue, a #6 round, a #4 bright, a #6 flat, a #4 oval/cat's tongue, a #2 spotter, a #4 round, and a #2 round.

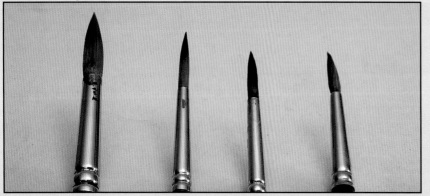

Figure 4.4. These detail brushes are made from natural hair, making them a bit more expensive than the base coat brushes in Figure 4.3. Pictured from left to right are a #8 7020 Loew Cornell round, a #4 7020 Loew Cornell round, a #3 Kolinsky round, and a #2 7020 Loew Cornell ultra round.

Figure 4.5. Fan blenders work well for blending two colors together. Pictured from left to right are a #4, a #12, a #10, a #8, and a #6 fan blender.

Figure 4.6. This set of brushes is used for blending. Pictured from left to right are a large mop, a #12 round, a ⅜" blender, and a #6 Badger beveled flat.

Inexpensive brushes: When painting acrylics on a rough surface, I use less expensive brushes to apply the base coats. "Soft grip" brushes are very reasonably priced and work well (see **Figure 4.3**).

Detail brushes: I use several detail brushes (see **Figure 4.4**). My favorites are a #4 7020 Loew Cornell ultra round and a #5 Kalinsky.

Fan brushes: Blending brushes consist of fans in a variety of sizes (see **Figure 4.5**).

Stipple and mop blenders: The stipple blender (see **Figure 4.6**) is used to do up and down stipple blending. The mop blenders are used to soften two colors by dragging this brush between the two, making a blended color in the area between them, known as the transition area.

One final thought before we begin: This bird can be totally block painted and then antiqued, and it will still look fine. This species can be very intimidating with all of the color, but I want the bird to remain bright and intense. That way, when I go to antique the bird, the antiquing process will then dull the colors down to their correct values. Thus, some of the initial colors will look bright to you. The antiquing process will take care of that. With that said, let's start painting.

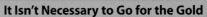

MASTER TIP

It Isn't Necessary to Go for the Gold
When selecting synthetic nylon brushes, the only difference between gold talkon and white talkon is that the white becomes stained, whereas the gold stays gold. Since the staining will not affect your painting in any way, choosing white talkon brushes can be an effective way to keep costs down.

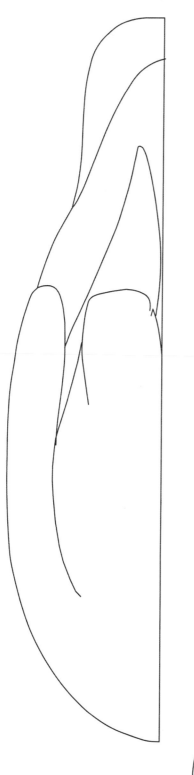

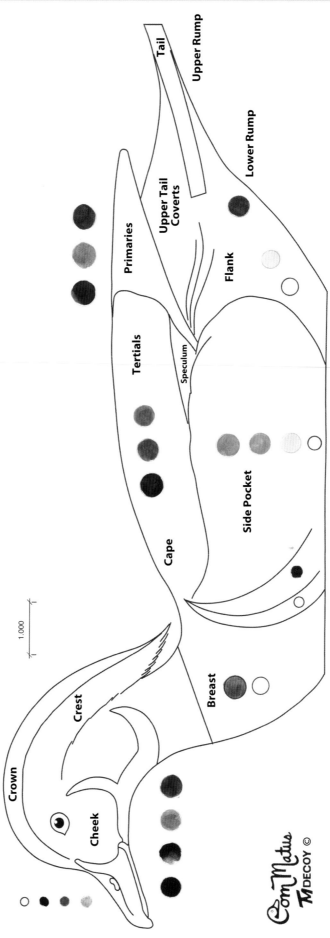

The dots represent the final colors for the various areas of the wood duck. Using the basic pigments recommended, mix the paints until the right color appears on your palette. Be aware that different manufacturers' paints and different proportions will produce a varied spectrum. This chart is only a guide and is not meant as a hard-and-fast recipe for producing the exact colors of this bird; rather, it is meant to come close to the colors of the real bird.

Crown

Crest

Cheek

Cape

Breast

Tertials

Speculum

Side Pocket

Primaries

Upper Tail Coverts

Flank

Lower Rump

Upper Rump

Tail

1.000

Com Mature
TM DECOY ©

Paint conversion chart

If you prefer to use oils or if you want to use a different brand of paint, this chart will provide you with the necessary information to check that you have the correct corresponding color. For example, if you are looking for a corresponding color to napthol red, the pigment code tells you that you need a paint with a pigment (P) in the red color group (R) with a chemical makeup assigned the number 170. The correct corresponding color would have PR170 written on the container. Opacity and temperature are also given for your reference.

Paint list for wood duck drake			
Color name	Pigment code	Opacity	Temperature
Titanium white	PW 6	Opaque	Neutral
Warm white	PW 6, PY 42	Opaque	Warm
Yellow oxide	PY 42	Opaque	Warm
Raw sienna	PBr 7	Semi-transparent	Warm
Raw umber	PBr 7	Opaque	Warm
Burgundy	Manufacturer mix	Opaque	Warm
Phthalo green-blue	PG 7	Semi-transparent	Neutral
Phthalo blue	PB 15:3	Semi-transparent	Neutral
Napthol red	PR 170	Semi-transparent	Cool
Carbon black	PBk 7	Opaque	Neutral/cool
Burnt sienna	PBr 7	Opaque	Warm
Burnt umber	PBr 7	Opaque	Warm
Light grey value 8	Manufacturer mix	Opaque	Cool
Ultramarine blue	PB 29	Semi-transparent	Warm
Medium green	Manufacturer mix	Opaque	Neutral
Dioxazine purple	PV 23	Transparent	Warm
Hansa yellow	PY 74	Semi-transparent	Neutral
Phthalo green-yellow	PG 36	Semi-transparent	Neutral
Perinone orange	PO 43	Transparent	Warm

Mediums	
Glaze	This is a clear matte glaze that is used between detail coats to be used as a barrier coat or before final varnishing and aging.
Extender	This medium is used to increase the "open" time you have to blend and work with the paint.
Texture paste	This will add body and impasto characteristics to any color paint. It allows the paint to peak and hold texture from a brush or comb.

Reference for this section is from "JansenArt Traditions Artist's Technical Guide," produced by David Jansen, 2003 MDA and DecoArt, Inc. Used with permission.

Common painting terms

Base coat, or blocking in – These two terms mean the same thing. The first step in all painting is to block in, or base coat, a mid-tone value of the decoy. Then, you begin applying the next values of color to create the form and depth of each feather group. With acrylics I paint light to dark.

Block painting – Style of painting which uses large blocks of color for the different parts of the decoy. Often involves fewer transitional blends between the various areas.

Double loading or triple loading – This simply refers to a procedure where you put two or more colors on different parts of your brush. You mix these colors on the canvas instead of on your palette. This is used more for wet-on-wet techniques with large areas of coverage and larger brushes. Creates a very soft, subtle effect with one-stroke coverage.

Dry brushing – Load a brush with a certain color, a highlight or a shadow. Remove a majority of the paint from the brush with a lint-free cloth and then lightly touch the area of the decoy to which you want to add paint. Use a very light touch for this technique. Used to highlight or shadow facial and individual feather features.

Extender – An additive, or medium, added to any paint to extend drying time. Allows more time for blending.

Glazing – A barrier coat over detailed painting used to protect the sub-layers from movement when additional layers are applied. Not to be confused with a wash.

Ragging – Once a decoy is stained or washed and the decoy is dry but not cured, you use a rag with solvent (water or spirits) to remove the thin, dry layer on top. This removes some paint to allow the peaks to show. I use this on combed and stippled areas. Works on areas of vermiculation.

Rough blending – A base coat blend that does not need to be neat or refined.

Shuttle blending – Technique where you apply two colors onto a decoy and then use a fan blender to gradually conduct the blending on the surface of the decoy, not the palette. This is usually done on the base coat of a bird. The first step is to apply the paint in a horizontal manner and then gently wipe through this blend with a separate dampened brush to create brush marks. Adds great detail.

Staining – Oil paint is thinned down with dirty spirits to create a very thin but potent paint. This stain will invade small cracks and imperfections so that the grain of the wood or the aging processes will show up. Helps create contrast. Works well when applied in limited areas.

Stippling – Technique of using a large brush in a vertical posture to blend paint with small dots, moving along the transition area to create a blend. Can be accomplished with more pressure when the paint is semi-dry. Can be accomplished if the paint is wet as well.

Straight color – Any color taken directly from the bottle and applied to a project without being thinned.

Texture paste – Thickening agent added to paint to provide loft.

Vermiculation – Small squiggles of variegated lines and dots that give an erratic barred pattern.

Washing – This technique is basically the opposite of dry brushing. Your paint is in a liquid form and will settle into the bottom texture and shadow those created voids.

Wet blending – Technique of blending while the colors are still wet.

Wet-on-dry blending – This technique is used most often in acrylic painting. Your base coat color is dry and you apply the topcoat over it by using one of the blending techniques, such as dry brushing, stippling, or washing.

Wet-on-wet blending – This technique is used when you're blending colors together while the first application of paint is still wet. Use of this technique is for initial blocking in or base coating the decoy. Adding extender will increase your open time.

Tinting the Decoy

Before we get into the real painting of the bird, we are going to tint the bird close to the color of the unfinished bird. This way, when we use the antiquing techniques on the decoy, the tint we add now will show through the sanding or scraping we do in subsequent steps.

Again, this step is only a wash of paint on raw wood; we want the paint to sink into the wood. You will see that the wood is going to absorb the paint quite quickly and readily, and (at times) the colors will be tough to blend. I recommend that you use plenty of water and put the paint in the exact place you want it to be. In subsequent steps, the original coating of paint will be covered over with lean applications of paint, but it will still show through. Use plenty of water and extender when adding the color.

Sketch the major feather groups on the decoy following the pattern provided on page 71. I suggest that you paint these parts of the bird first and then let it dry. This way you can read ahead and get a better feel for what you will have to do in the upcoming steps.

Using a large 1" brush, mix copious amounts of water with each of the following colors: burnt umber, titanium white, and carbon black. I use small condiment cups to mix the washes; they come in handy when making large amounts of wash.

Apply the burnt umber to the tail and black to the upper rump area. Rough blend the two colors. Then, on the lower rump, add titanium white closer to the bottom and burnt umber closer to the tail. Blend these two together. This section can be block painted as well because this is just an undercoat and will be painted over in subsequent layers. This will be your first of many chances to practice wet-on-wet blending.

Now add the burnt umber to the back, up to the cape. Use raw sienna on the side pocket and paint up to where the black and white barring is on the front.

Paint the breast with burnt sienna.
Use straight warm white on the head with straight titanium white, and then paint the head with a mix of 90% teal green and 10% carbon black. Coat the bill with straight titanium white. This will provide a good base for your paint.

This view shows the back of the head.

5

Here is a look at the head and back from the top. Notice that the grain shows through the paint.

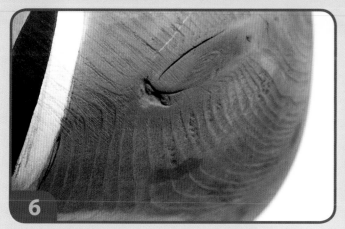

6

A close-up photograph shows the knot on the breast.

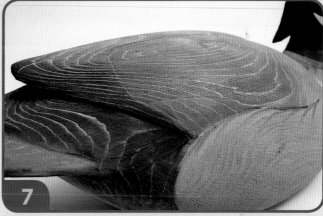

7

Notice the grain pattern where the primaries are. This is one example of getting lucky and having a "fingerprint" on a decoy. This attribute will not allow any other decoy to be confused with this one. It is a great look, and each decoy you make will take on a different one. Anytime you find these anomalies, be sure to pull them out of the decoy.

8

A close-up view of the side pocket shows how thin the paint is when it dries. You may have to paint this bird twice to get the color that you see in these photos. Let the bird dry overnight.

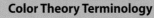

MASTER TIP

Color Theory Terminology

Hue – The undiluted true color as found in nature.

Color – Any hue.

Saturation – Brightness of a color. Stimulate an area, highlight.

Value – Lightness and darkness of a color.

Tint – A color when white is added, lighter shade of a color. Pink is a tint of any reddish color.

Shade – A color when black is added; darker shade of a color. Navy is a shade of blue. You can also add the complement of the original color to get a harmonious shadowing effect, such as adding orange to blue.

COMBING THE SIDE POCKET

Prior to base coating and painting the decoy, we will be required to comb the side pocket and let the decoy sit for at least four hours. This is a tedious process that can have adverse consequences if rushed.

Before we jump right into the combing, let me first describe what I will be doing in this step. Review this series of procedures before you actually attempt it on the decoy. The process requires a small amount of skill and some quickness. You will take a thicker, impasto-like paint, neatly apply it over the side pocket with a paintbrush, and then, starting at the back of the side pocket, move from top to bottom to make a series of zigzag lines.

Note: Do not try to force dry this step because you may crack the texture paste and ruin the finish. Also, I recommend that you practice on a spare, sealed piece of wood if you have not tried this procedure before. You may also skip this style of vermiculation and hand paint the feather pattern later.

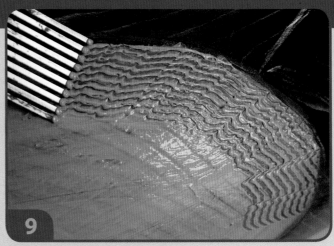

Combs can be purchased from many decoy carving supply stores. The comb pictured here is from The Duck Blind and is made of thin spring steel. When you move a comb through the thicker paint, it pulls paint from the bird and creates small grooves.

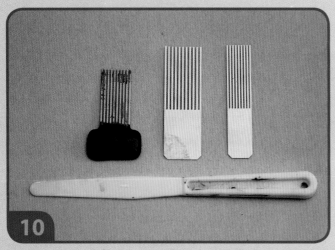

Here is a selection of combs I use. The palette knife shown below the combs is used to mix and spread the texture paste and paint.

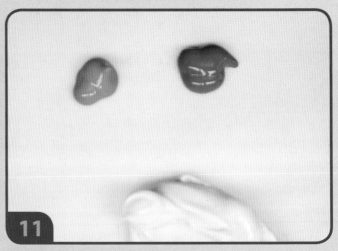

I placed yellow oxide to the left and raw sienna to the right. Texture medium from JansenArt is mixed with these two paints.

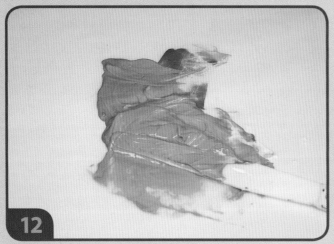

The texture paste is mixed up and ready to be applied to the side pocket.

Apply the texture paste to the side pocket in a uniform thickness. This consistency should be like sour cream.

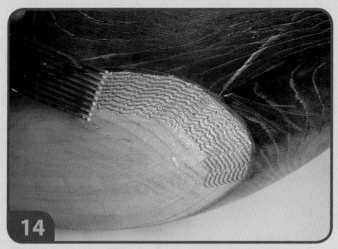

14

Start the comb at the back and begin your zigzag lines.

15

The side pocket is completed. Let this section dry now for at least four hours. I usually let it dry overnight (about 8 to 10 hours). Adding water and paint to it before the four hours is up will only reactivate the paste, and you will lose the loft and pattern you made on the decoy.

MASTER TIP

Mastering Vermiculation
Prior to combing your bird, place a lint-free towel close by to wipe off the excess paint that the comb removes so you achieve cleaner vermiculation marks. Each pass builds up texture paste on the comb, and, if the buildup is not removed, subsequent tracks will not come out very well.

The first areas to be painted will be the upper rump, the upper tail coverts, the tail, the lower rump, and the flank. Notice the hard lines for this area are the side pocket and the primaries. A big blend occurs between the upper rump and the tail, and another blend occurs between the lower rump and the upper rump, with some burgundy between the two areas. The top edge has a few wispy orange-gold feathers that hang down—one very distinct trait of the wood duck that will be added during the detail phase.

Lay out the colors you will need on your palette. Pictured, right to left, are warm white, burgundy, raw umber, and phthalo green-blue. I have added water and a small amount of extender to these paints.

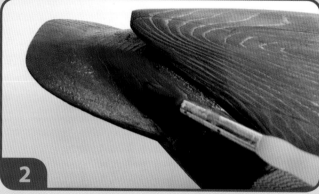

Using a #6 round synthetic brush, place phthalo green-blue and raw umber on the tail and upper tail coverts and blend them. Add a small amount of carbon black to add shadows and depth to this area.

MASTER TIP

Optimizing Acrylic Paints
Acrylic paints lend themselves to either opaque or transparent characteristics. To optimize their abilities, I have found that, when painting decoys, you want to build with layers, tinting with transparent washes and detailing with opaque. Building the intensity of the decoy's color should be from light to dark to enhance its look. Practice adding light feather tips and then putting a thinned coat of paint over them to change their color. Doing this will add softness to your decoy's finish.

Tail and rump paint colors

The swatches below are references against which you can compare the sections that you are painting. I have offered percentages as guidelines to get you started; however, you should always judge your colors and blends based on your reference materials and personal taste.

Upper Tail Coverts
Phthalo green-blue – 75%
Raw umber – 20%
Carbon black – 5%

Tail
Phthalo green-blue – 75%
Raw umber – 20%
Carbon black – 5%

Flank Feathers
Burgundy – 75%
Burnt sienna – 25%

Upper Rump
Burnt umber – 100%

Lower Rump
Warm white – 90%
Raw umber – 10%
Touch of carbon black

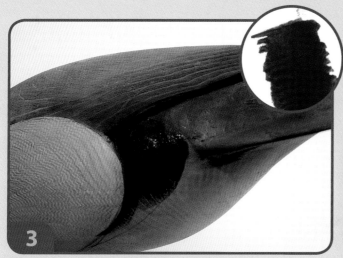

3 Apply burgundy and burnt sienna to the flank area and blend the two colors together. Using a fan blender or flat brush of choice, shuttle blend where the flank feathers and the upper tail coverts meet (inset). Paint the upper rump with straight burnt umber.

4 Now mix warm white, raw umber, and a touch of carbon black on the lower rump.

5 The tail region should look like this now. Make sure that the blended areas are nice and soft and that the lower rump is just a shade off bright white. You may need to add titanium white to the center lower portion of the rump to give it depth. Evaluate the look once you get farther along. This can be done during the detailing process.

6 Where the dark burgundy and white come together, take a small #6 or #8 flat brush, double load it with paint on both sides, and shuttle blend between the two colors.

7 Apply that brush to the block-painted region and soft-feather blend them together. To create a soft-feathered blend, hold the brush perpendicular to the line and move the brush over the line with small up-and-down movements, wiggling it back and forth as you blend the two colors.

8 Notice the clean appearance of a soft-feathered blend.

PRIMARY FEATHERS

Of all of the puddle ducks, the wood duck has some of the most distinct and noticeable primary feathers, also known as flight feathers. These are the long protruding feathers at the tips of his wings. They have a leading edge of whitish gray with a blue tint. The base color for the trailing edge will be ultramarine blue with some raw umber, white, and black added.

As this paint dries, we will edge the primaries before moving on so that the subsequent applications of paint will make the feather edging stand out crisp and clean.

Primary feathers paint colors

The swatches below are references against which you can compare the sections that you are painting. I have offered percentages as guidelines to get you started; however, you should always judge your colors and blends based on your reference materials and personal taste.

Leading Edge Primaries
Titanium white – 70%
Light grey value 8 – 30%

Note: If you don't have light grey value 8, you can make the leading edge primaries color with 2% ultramarine blue, 3% carbon black, and 95% titanium white.

Trailing Edge Primaries
Titanium white – 5%
Raw umber – 10%
Carbon black – 5%
Ultramarine blue – 80%

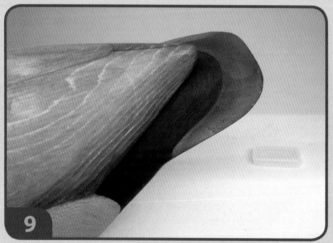

9

Lay out the primaries in pencil. This step is critical, so be careful of the lines and the balance of the location. You may need to use a smaller brush with a slightly thicker paint and extender to get the edges to contrast and stand out.

10

Using titanium white and light grey value 8, create the lighter gray-blue color on the leading edge of the primary.

11

Now apply ultramarine blue, raw umber, titanium white, and carbon black to paint the top (trailing edge) of the feather with the darker gray-blue color.

SECONDARIES

The secondaries, or speculum, are the very bright feathers that become exposed when the side pocket drops or the wing is held high. On content poses, the speculum will usually be hidden, but, in this semi-alert upright pose, we will show it. This is a great place to demonstrate your knowledge of the color wheel and display a powerful area of the bird. I like to take advantage of painting the speculum whenever I can. As we paint the secondaries, we will also add highlights to both edges of the primaries.

On the secondaries, it is my preference to make them stand out and be noticed. I will make them brilliant in this step because, once again, the antiquing process will dull them tremendously. Trust me, I know this from trial and error; the whole bird will end up light overall. Not taking into account the effects of the antiquing process is a common mistake on attempts to create aging decoys. Do not get me wrong—decoys can be very dark, and, if that is the look you want to go for, feel free. However, the wood duck is a beautiful, striking bird, so, for this project, let's make him bright, as if he has been taken care of after hunting and then brought into the home for off-season viewing.

MASTER TIP

Using Iridescent Paints and Powders

One area of controversy when creating an antique-style decoy is whether or not to stick with the paint of the era you're drawing inspiration from or to modernize it. Some modern-day carvers like to add metal flakes of iridescences to the paint. If you are going to make this bird look old, I'd suggest staying away from iridescent paint since I am unsure if this paint was available 20 or 40 yeas ago. Depending on your own style, you can add some of this paint to your decoy, but make sure that the corresponding style equates to the paint era. Some people like to see the whole bird reflected within the same era. You might try a second bird with iridescence and then compare the two. This step is a great place to inject your own style. For this demonstration, I added a small amount of iridescence to accentuate the colorful drake wood duck's head feathers.

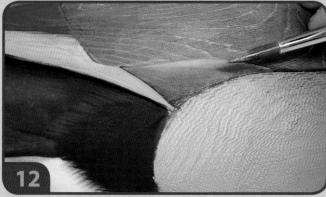

12

Using extender, dampen the speculum so that the colors will blend. Apply phthalo blue and titanium white with a #8 7020 Loew Cornell or a small flat brush.

Secondary feathers paint colors

The swatches below are references against which you can compare the sections that you are painting. I have offered percentages as guidelines to get you started; however, you should always judge your colors and blends based on your reference materials and personal taste.

Speculum
Phthalo blue – 50%
Titanium white – 50%

Trailing Edge Primary Highlight
Phthalo blue – 80%
Carbon black – 20%

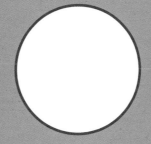

Trailing Edge Primary Highlight
Titanium white – 100%

Secondary Edges
Titanium white – 100%

Secondary Edges
Carbon black – 100%

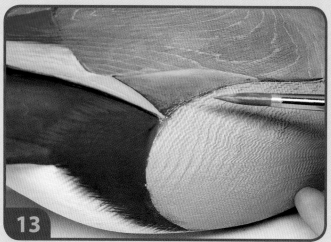

13

Blend the colors. At the lower portion, where the speculum meets the previously painted primary, paint a thin stripe of straight phthalo blue, and blend the colors with the tip of the #8 7020 Loew Cornell or a small flat brush. Your end result should be a speculum that is bluest where it borders the side pocket and the primary and lightest where it borders the tertials.

14

Load a #2 liner with a mixture of phthalo blue and carbon black to line the trailing edge of the primary.

15

Clean the same brush and load it with thinned titanium white. Edge the leading edge of the primary. A clean line is good, but if the line is uneven or crooked, that's okay. This can be an area that is heavily aged or worn.

16

On the secondaries, using straight titanium white, make three quick, clean, comma-like edges on the clean blue feathers using a #2 7020 Loew Cornell. Then, edge the marks with carbon black.

MASTER TIP

The Perfect Painting Environment

To get paint to flow freely from your brush, add a small amount of extender directly onto your brush prior to painting; wipe off the excess and start to paint. Be sure to limit the amount of breeze or airflow in your painting area. The surface breeze helps evaporate the water from acrylics and shortens your drying time. Also, try to paint when humidity and heat are low. Minimize hot overhead lighting.

TERTIALS

Now that we have successfully painted the primaries and the secondaries, we can move on to the tertials, cape, and breast. There will be multiple blends between the various regions. The live bird has a dark, almost blue-black set of tertials up to the cape, which then turn a deep brown-green before the burgundy breast. We will apply the paint for these three regions one at a time and then blend the transition areas.

Starting at the tertials, paint the outside edge with phthalo blue using a 1" flat synthetic brush. Add a little bit of carbon black to the phthalo blue to create depth and shadows. The inside color in this photo is phthalo green-blue. We will be adding the medium green highlight immediately after we've lined the tertials with the first two colors, so be sure to work quickly during this process.

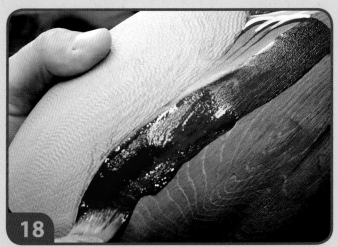

Continue to apply the paint. You can either apply the paints on the bird and blend the color right there on the decoy or double load the brush with two colors and apply multiple colors with one swipe.

Tertial feathers paint colors

The swatches below are references against which you can compare the sections that you are painting. I have offered percentages as guidelines to get you started; however, you should always judge your colors and blends based on your reference materials and personal taste.

Outside Edge
Phthalo blue – 80%
Carbon black – 20%

Inside Edge
Phthalo green-blue – 100%

Highlight
Medium green – 100%

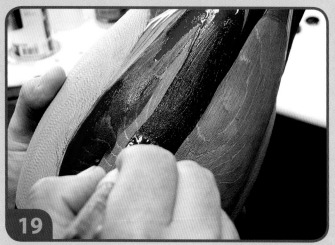

19 Continue to apply phthalo blue and phthalo green-blue to the tertials.

20 Add the medium green highlight in the middle with a #6 round synthetic brush.

21 Using a stiff hog bristle brush, shuttle blend the colors together. Blend in one direction (try not to sweep back and forth), and then back into and out of the same area. A back-and-forth motion will make only one color in the end—mud brown!

MASTER TIP

Blending with Washes
Washes can be used to tint or tone a feather group, and they can be a great way to tone down a hen carving. When applying a wash, blend it to water so that there is a transition of tone. Straight washes will create an abrupt color edge where they stop. Remember, less is more when applying a wash. You can always add another layer of wash if you are not satisfied with the way it looks. Too much color, however, is tough to remove.

The cape is a deep brown-green close to the back and brown-purple near the breast blend. This area will require two blend brushes. Be prepared and lay out the brushes in advance so that, when the two areas are ready to blend, you have a brush ready to use.

When applying paint to the breast area, keep in mind that the cape should still be wet. Remember to apply up to 20 percent of extender to any paint to keep it blendable.

Cape and breast paint colors

The swatches below are references against which you can compare the sections that you are painting. I have offered percentages as guidelines to get you started; however, you should always judge your colors and blends based on your reference materials and personal taste.

Back Cape
Raw umber – 80%
Phthalo green-blue – 20%

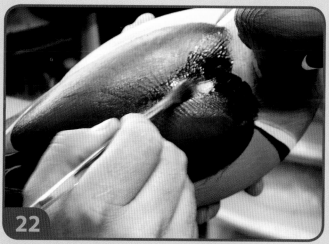

Add raw umber and phthalo green-blue to the back of the cape with a large #6 or #8 round brush.

Front Cape
Burgundy – 70%
Raw umber – 30%

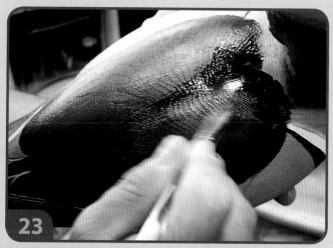

Now blend this color to the tertials color. **Note:** Blending brushes should be dampened with extender and then wiped off on a lint-free towel for better use. Each time you blend, blend in one direction and then wipe; blend again in one direction and wipe. The quicker you routinely wipe out your brush, the less chance you have of making mud out of your paint.

Breast
Burgundy – 60%
Dioxazine purple – 30%
Carbon black – 10%

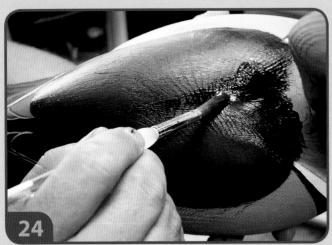

24 Continue to blend and smooth out the transition.

25 Now, quickly use burgundy and raw umber, mixed together, to blend the cape to the breast. Put paint near the transition area where it can be easily blended. Use a #6 flat brush for this task.

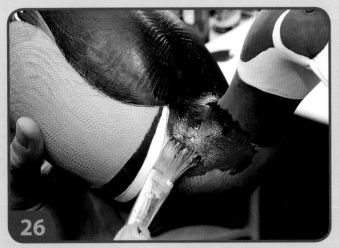

26 Place the burgundy, dioxazine purple, and carbon black on the bird to create the breast color. Start to blend the breast color into the cape color.

27 As you are blending around the bib, be careful not to get too much paint on the white area. It will be tough to cover in later steps.

28 The blending is finished on the first coat. If you applied paint too thinly, you may need to add a second coat. Apply the second coat only after this section has dried. You may use a hair dryer on low heat to accelerate the drying time.

SIDE POCKET

We are closer to completion. After evaluating the reference photos and live wood ducks, I see that a wide variety of colors can be displayed in the side pocket. Again, thinking ahead, we are going to be darkening the whole decoy, and this side pocket will need to stay lighter yellow in order to look lifelike. So, I have elected to use yellow oxide as the mid-tone value. I will darken it with raw sienna and lighten it with warm white. Both values are harmonious to the overall color we are trying to achieve. A nice, warm, golden color is our final target.

Side pocket paint colors

The swatches below are references against which you can compare the sections that you are painting. I have offered percentages as guidelines to get you started; however, you should always judge your colors and blends based on your reference materials and personal taste.

Upper Side Pocket
Raw sienna – 100%

Middle Side Pocket
Yellow oxide – 100%

Lower Side Pocket
Warm white – 100%

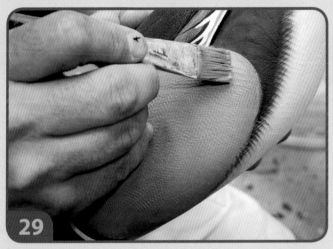

29

Apply raw sienna to the top half of the side pocket, yellow oxide through the middle, and warm white on the bottom using a 3/4" flat brush. Blend all three colors together to start to create our warm, golden color. Be mindful of the top and back of the side pocket. There are hard lines and overlaps here that can be slightly messy, but other areas require clean, precise lines. All of this blending is helping us to get ready to paint the head, which is the toughest area to blend.

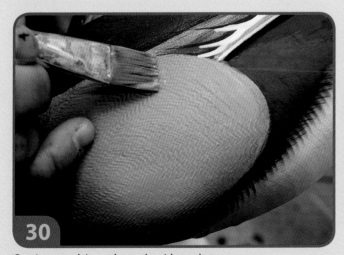

30

Continue applying color to the side pocket.

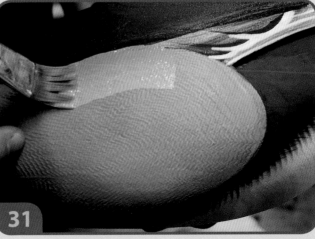

31

Here, I have double loaded the brush with two colors, raw sienna for the top section of the bird and yellow oxide for the middle of the side pocket. Shuttle blend the two colors together.

32

Add warm white to the lower portion of the side pocket. If you feel you can handle the double load, load the brush with warm white and yellow oxide and apply the blended color.

33

Shuttle blend. I am using a large #12 fan blender.

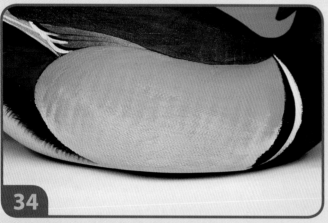

34

Here is what the finished side pocket should look like. I am trying to achieve a soft look with neither streaking nor harsh, abrupt color changes.

MASTER TIP

The Best Days to Paint
Weather conditions will affect your painting characteristics. Cool, rainy days will help extend the open period during which you can blend paints. Low temperatures and minimal sun or overhead lights will also allow paints to be blended for longer periods of time.

35

Look how much we have completed!

THE HEAD

The head of a drake wood duck is very colorful and powerful. You can use color in this area to brighten and enhance all of the colors used on the entire decoy, making a vivid statement that will aid the aging and antiquing. Reference material at this point is extremely important since the painting of the head will require much attention to detail.

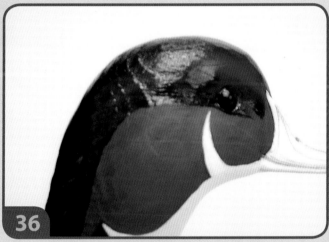

Begin laying in phthalo green-blue, phthalo green-yellow, and medium green. Blend, using whatever brush you find most comfortable. Be careful around the bill area since stray colors can be tough to cover when you are painting the bill in the next step.

Add more phthalo green-yellow and add phthalo blue near the face and blend. Don't worry about getting paint on the eye.

Head paint colors

The swatches below represent all of the colors that you will use to paint the head. I have noted the general sections in which the colors are used; however, these are only guidelines. Because the head is a blend of so many different colors, be sure to use the photos here, your reference materials, and your own judgment to create the finished, blended head.

Cheek and Crown Highlight
Hansa yellow – 100%

Cheeks and Mid-Crown
Medium green – 100%

Rear Cheek and Crest
Phthalo green-yellow – 100%

Crest and Shadows
Phthalo green-blue – 100%

Shadows and Crown
Phthalo blue – 100%

Front Cheek
Dioxazine purple – 100%

38 Add a highlight of phthalo green-yellow and hansa yellow on the crown and rear cheek. Blend it in.

39 Add more phthalo blue and dioxazine purple to the cheek. If you have painted over the eye and the paint is still wet, you can wipe off the paint with a soft cloth. Any paint that has dried on the eye can be gently scraped off with a dampened toothpick.

40 Continue to blend the crest.

41 I have added a small amount of dry iridescent blue powder to the eye trough to illuminate the head. Though some carvers believe that metal flake paint should not be included in an antique bird, I included iridescent powder in the final applications of head paint because the head did not come alive without it when compared to what I saw in the reference photos. As an artist, I want to paint what I see and capture how the duck reflects light.

42 The head is finished up and ready for detail.

43 Here is where we are now. The white bib, or chin strap, under the chin of the bird will be added later with titanium white.

BILL

The bill of a drake wood duck is complex, but this project will simplify it. The angles and proportions of the white and black need to be within the limits of what the actual bird has. Otherwise, your own eyes will play tricks on your mind and provide an optical illusion that you don't want, such as a drooping bill, incorrect angles, or an incorrect thickness. So, the placement of all of the colors needs to be more accurate than just a guess; pay attention to your reference material.

When painting the bill, you want to make sure that all of the hard lines that hit the face and the crown are even and symmetrical. As you apply the paint, be sure that the colors are evenly placed on the bill. Make adjustments accordingly.

44

Neatly cut in a mixture of yellow oxide, raw sienna, and gesso along the bill, close to the face, using a #4 round brush. Use the reference photos as your model. This may require two or three coats. You will also notice that the yellow is tough to cover. The lesson to be learned here is "be neat."

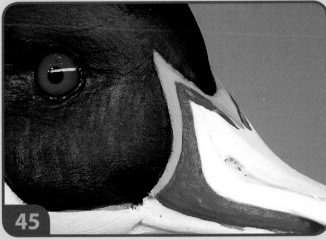

45

Add napthol red next to the yellow and neatly line the upper/lower mandible separation. The lower portion of the bill will be black, so you can clean the line up if there is a mistake.

Bill paint colors

The swatches below are references against which you can compare the sections that you are painting. I have offered percentages as guidelines to get you started; however, you should always judge your colors and blends based on your reference materials and personal taste.

Upper Bill Detail
Yellow oxide – 75%
Raw sienna – 20%
Gesso – 5%

Mandible Highlight
Napthol red – 100%

Mantle, Nail, and Lower Mandible
Carbon black – 100%

Bill and Bib
Titanium white – 100%

46

Add two coats of titanium white to the white area on the side of the head and lower chin (bib). **Note:** Two or three thin coats are better than one very thick coat. Be patient with this area.

47

Neatly add carbon black to the mantle, nail, and lower mandible area.

48

Touch up as required, and then add one coat of glaze over the bill.

MASTER TIP

Dry Brushing

Dry brushing is a skill that will come with time. I recommend practicing on paper towels when you are first learning. Always remember to wipe out your brush so that very little paint comes off. When you are dry brushing any shadows or highlights, practicing the idea of "less is more" will get you better results.

49

Here, we have the head blended softly, and the bill is blocked in. Now, neatly repaint the white area with titanium white.

DETAILS

Again, we will start from the tail and work our way forward to complete the bird. The colors to be used will be noted within each area. The details are added with a pointed detail brush. Most painters have a favorite detail brush, and I suggest getting comfortable with the brushes you have. Also, at this point, when adding details, make sure the color you are adding is the color you want in the final product. You cannot go back in and tint or alter the color. You may have to test a color by painting on a piece of paper and placing it next to the area you are going to paint. Or, better yet, let the decoy dry, glaze the area where you are going to paint, and then practice. If you glaze it and give the affected area overnight to dry, you can paint on the area, evaluate it, and (if you decide to) remove the paint in a few minutes. Before you attempt this, make sure that the area is completely dry. Its being even slightly damp could ruin prior painting efforts.

Edge the tail with carbon black, watered down slightly to get the paint to flow. In the photo, I am using a #4 7020 Loew Cornell brush.

With titanium white, using the same brush that you used in the previous step, add the white edge to the tertial. Be sure to clean out the brush very well.

With perinone orange, add the wispy flank feathers.

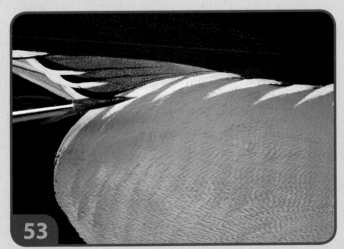

Using the reference photos and the pattern, lay out the carbon black and the titanium white bars on the top of the side pocket. Add white first.

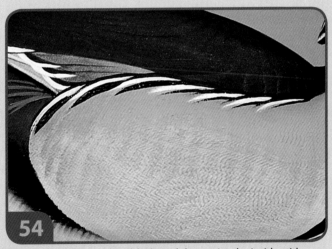

Paint the top edge carbon black, and then paint the inside with carbon black.

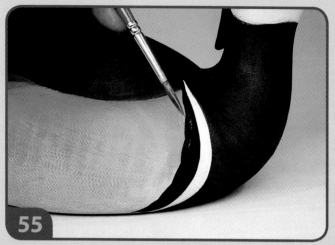

55

Clean up the front shoulder bars with titanium white.

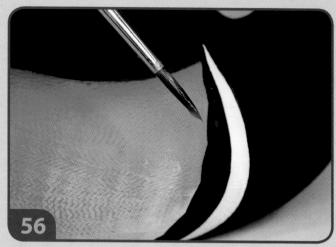

56

Now clean up the black shoulder bars with carbon black. These are adjacent to the white you previously added.

57

Paint the white triangles on the breast with titanium white. I recommend laying them out with a watercolor pencil and staggering the lines. Start at the top and work your way down the breast. The smaller feather patterns are at the top, and they get progressively larger as you get to the bottom of the breast. I use a #2 7020 Loew Cornell for this detail.

58

Now paint the bib on the bird with titanium white. Also add titanium white to the lower crest feathers, using the pattern as a reference.

59

Add the top feathers along the crown with titanium white. Be sure to leave a gap about one-third of the way back. There is a short area here where no feathers of the crown overlap and no white shows. Use your reference material, and be as symmetrical as possible with this.

60

Now add a clean napthol red ring around the eye, and the decoy is done.

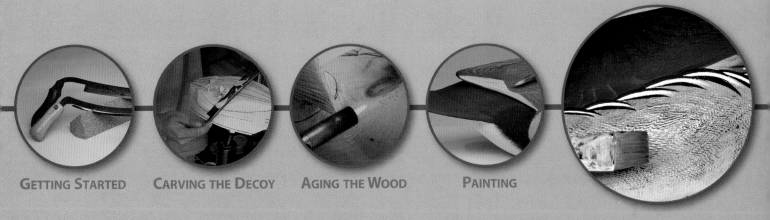

CHAPTER 5

GETTING STARTED   CARVING THE DECOY   AGING THE WOOD   PAINTING

ANTIQUING

Now that the wood duck decoy has made it through the final steps of painting, it is time to think about how we are going to age the decoy and how much wear and tear the decoy will have on it.

Prior to painting, we stressed the decoy some. One reason we stress the decoy before we paint is that many carvers who start with a project like this end it right about here. They have put a few hours into painting the bird and now decide that the bird looks very good. They would rather not add anything that will ruin or disrupt the paint job. (If you feel this way, I do understand where you're coming from. While making the decoy in this demonstration, my wife wanted me to leave it "as is.")

One suggestion I have is that you might want to practice on a spare piece of wood that you painted similar to this decoy. That might ease your concerns. Before I proceeded to apply any of these antiquing processes on the demonstration decoy, I made sure that the processes worked on a practice board.

You may have wanted to create this kind of decoy in the past after seeing someone else's and wondered how to accomplish its "look" or "style." You may have also asked a considerable number of other carvers how they do it, but the process was sidestepped or the issue was skirted. I strongly suggest that if there is a technique you like or have seen in the past, try to experiment and figure it out for yourself. Just copying another style is less rewarding than figuring it out yourself. Much of your success depends on the ambition and desire you have for creating a decoy with your own imprint. If you follow this path, the finished product will likely have more of you within it, and that—as well as your own accomplishment—is something of which you can be proud. My suggestion to you is take advice from and observe the work of many carvers; then, take the areas you like and adapt them to your own bird.

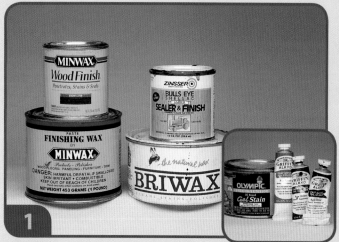

1

Because this bird was painted with acrylics, I will go over it with acrylics, then oil paints, then a fine furniture wax. You can put oils over acrylics, but not acrylics over oils. The water from the acrylics will try to dry through the oils and, as a result, chip or crack the paint from the surface. Here are some of the finishing waxes and paints that will be applied during this antiquing process.

2

Secret tools for stress and aging: Scotch-Brite and sandpaper.

3

In this photo, I am thinning JansenArt burnt umber with water and applying the watered-down mixture over just the side pocket to accentuate the combed vermiculation. I use a ½" flat brush for this task.

4

Continue to add the burnt umber until it has completely covered the side pocket. This may take two coats, depending on how dark you want the vermiculation to be.

Master Tip

Adding Years to a Decoy

Step 3 in itself can be used as a technique to make the decoy look older. Simply rub this thinned mixture over the whole bird and let it dry some. Rub the surface lightly with a soft cloth. The paint that fell into the cracks and sandpaper marks will stay and then the surface paint will be rubbed off. You can also use burlap and water to remove some of the paint. Some carvers stop at this process and call the decoy finished, but we can go a bit further to age the bird.

5

The side pocket has dried for about 15 minutes now. Take a relatively stiff towel or burlap and wipe the side pocket to remove the higher bumps created by the combing. I have only removed paint from the lower half of the side pocket. See the difference?

6

Here is the side pocket with all of the surface paint removed. See how it now stands out? Notice the wiggle lines start to show.

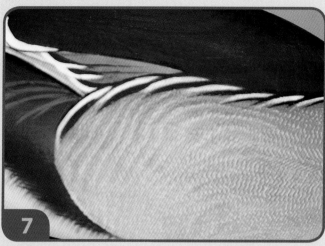

7

Here is a close-up photograph of the finished side pocket.

8

Now, to give the whole bird some aged, worn areas, you can go back to dropping the bird onto the stones and gravel or dropping a chain on it for smoother dings and dents, like we did earlier in Chapter 3, "Aging the Wood," on page 65. I also selectively place wear marks on the bird with 150-grit sandpaper. These marks go on the bill, tail, sides, cheeks, and primaries—areas of the bird that would normally see wear.

9

This photo shows the bottom of the decoy. Notice the subtle wear marks that I've created on the edge of the bottom using sandpaper.

10

Here is a look at the aging that has been created near the primary feathers.

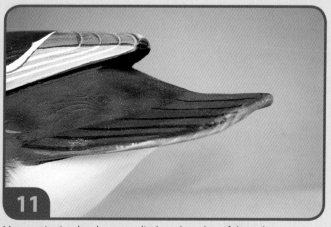

11

More antiquing has been applied on the edge of the tail.

12

Another idea from real hunting rigor is line marks. I use a heavily tarred line and wrap the bird. I then hit the crossing areas with a small hammer to show that something may have been set on or against this decoy during its use.

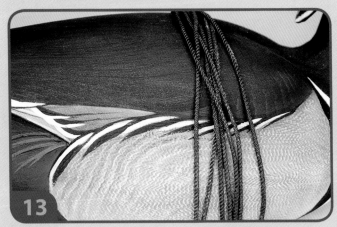

13

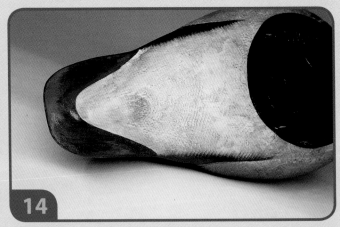

14

You could also wrap the body with the line and make a few lines on the decoy that way. This could show a different style of line wrap, and you may create a mark of your own that all of your birds have. If that is how you wrap your decoys when you hunt, why not incorporate that into your style?

I also go back and add more heat to certain areas to make the knots and grain lines pop. This may blister the paint as well. Blistering is okay, but don't go overboard.

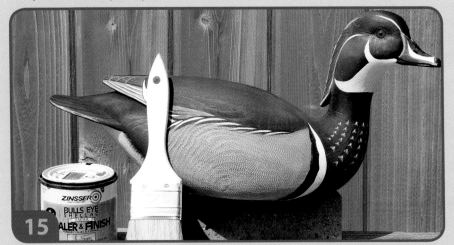

15

Once you have decided that your decoy has enough stress marks, the next step is to add an instant patina. Put amber shellac over the whole bird using an inexpensive 2" brush. This shellac is alcohol based and will dry quickly. As it is drying, rub areas that might be void of patina and add extra shellac to areas where it would accumulate. This is when the bird starts to come alive and you know that this process is worth the risk. Once the shellac starts to become very sticky, let it sit and dry. You can't rush this process.

16

The entire bird has been painted with amber shellac. **Note:** If you have trouble removing the shellac in the subsequent steps, try using a rag or a Scotch-Brite pad dampened with rubbing alcohol.

17

Now that the shellac is dry, rub a lint-free cloth across the bird. Rub hardest in the areas where you want the paint to show, lightest in the areas where you want the patina present. This is a personal preference. I like the golden color on the side pocket, and I prefer the white areas to have only some coloration.

18

This shellac is the first sealer we have added to the bird other than the thin coats of paint used initially for tinting, the actual paint, and then the glaze coat. We must protect the bird with something, but that will come with a fine coat of wax at the end. First, we need to build up the softness of the bird. I take coats of alkyds, or fast-drying oils, thinned with dirty paint thinner and apply them over the bird for a few days to build layers of oil. The shine will disappear in a week or so, and the oils will add to the patina for years to come.

19

Continue to buff and wax the decoy over several days as if it were being used and cleaned.

20

Closeup of the tail. Notice the decoy line marks in the right side of the photo in the burgundy color.

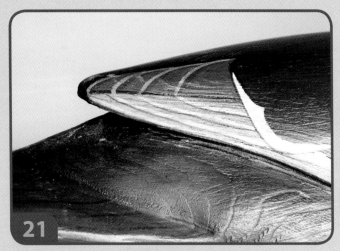

21

This closeup of the primary flight feathers shows how the grain looks. The lines and rings worked to our advantage.

22

Detail of the head and bill. Notice how the bill looks used and worn, with the dents that we added and the areas of paint that have been removed.

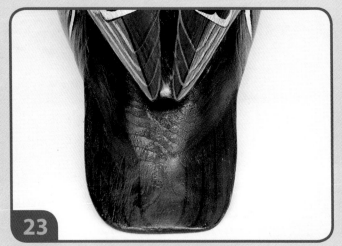

23

Marks on the top of the primaries show simulated wear on an area of the bird that would be rubbed during use in the field. This was accomplished with sandpaper and Scotch-Brite synthetic steel wool.

24

I have rubbed the knot under the rump more so it appears as if it has leaked some sap.

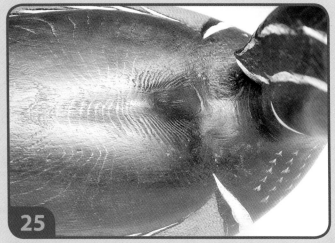

25

Again in the cape area, more brown paste wax has been rubbed into the knot to give the cracks of the knot depth and character.

26

Detailed view of the crest, where you see more rubbing has been done on the high spots and how the white paint fades and the green shows through. This is a good example of how you can expose layered paint, revealing how a painter actually painted the decoy.

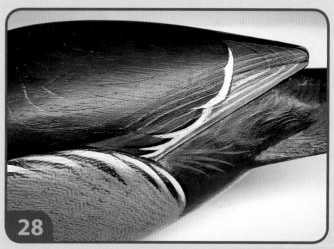

Marks around the neck from the anchor line were added with a tarred line and a small ball-peen hammer. Wrap the decoy like you would normally wrap a decoy anchor line and tap on the line in various spots as if the decoy was placed into a boat or a bag and had pressure placed on it to receive this sort of marking.

On the tertial area, I take a shard of glass and remove a thin layer of paint. Tape the area of the glass shard that you are holding so that you minimize the possibility of getting cut when performing this step. Do not remove too much paint with this procedure or it will look overdone.

ANTIQUING MEDIUMS AND ABRASION EQUIPMENT

This list of antiquing techniques will provide you with a quick reference and help get you started in your own techniques. My list continues to grow with each decoy I create. I recommend that you keep a list of your own so that you can catalog what you have tried and what techniques you like best. Discovering new methods is one of the most enjoyable parts of this type of project.

Antiquing material	Application	Effect
Oil paint, various colors (try raw sienna, burnt umber, and green)	Thin with water and applied with a brush	Accentuates textures and darkens color
Thinner (cheapest and dirtiest you can save and use)	Mix with alkyds and applied with a brush	Creates a patina, removes paint from bird
Bri Wax	Apply with cloth after all finishes are complete and buffed off	Appears used and cleaned, removes and softens paint, adds shine
Minwax Wood Stain	Brush all over decoy prior to painting	Darkens wood
Minwax Wood Gel	Brush on spots of decoy after painting	Darkens and mutes paint
Finishing Wax by Minwax	Apply with rag and buffed off	Provides protection for all previously added details
Amber shellac, sealer and finish	Brush over entire decoy after painting	Yellows the bird, protects the paint
Cedar ash (burnt cedar, homemade)	Rub over decoy as a rubbing compound	Reveals cracks and polishes
Decoy weights, various weights	Drop or hang on decoy	Creates dents or lead marks
Salt water, homemade	Soak decoy in mixture	Simulates corrosion
Decoy anchor line (various lines used to attach weights to decoys)	Tie to decoy and hit with hammer	Creates dents and wear marks
Rust	Moisten copper and iron to obtain dry rust particles and add to metal attached to decoy	Simulates rust
Copper BB (from shotgun shell)	Drop on decoy or imbed in decoy	Simulates decoy being shot
Lead pellet (from shotgun shell)	Drop on decoy or imbed in decoy	Simulates decoy being shot
Sandpaper	Sand the bird after painting	Rubs off paint and creates areas of wear
Burlap	Rub the decoy down	Looks as though it was loaded into burlap bag for years
Shard of glass	Scrape paint from decoy	Reveals the paint underneath the top layers

FINISHING TOUCHES

At this point, the bird is all but completed. I now like to look at the bird over a few days or weeks, evaluating what I see in the real bird and what I want to convey to the viewer with this decoy. A closer visual inspection will reveal smaller details that can be added to the overall look and feel of the decoy.

One part of the secret to making antique-style decoys is to have old hardware for the rigging. I collect all that I can from various places and store it outside in the elements. This way, when it comes time to add a leather tab or lead to the bottom of the decoy, the hardware will already look old and used.

To create a leather tab, I take a small piece of leather and cut it to size. Again, here is another opportunity to give the bird your own look and feel, so find a size that you like and go with that to create your style. The leather tab I cut for this decoy is pretty standard for me, about 15 mm wide and 80 mm long, then folded in half.

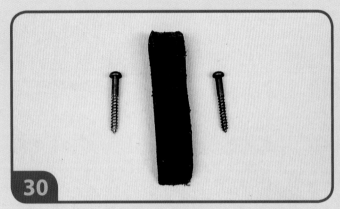

I predrill the holes in the leather and add two brass screws to secure the leather in place. Attach the leather tab.

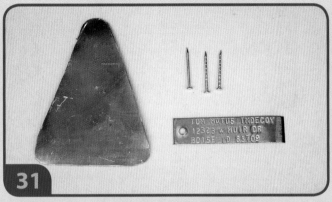

Now, the lead needs to be attached to the bottom of the decoy. I take a small amount of lead flashing and cut it to a spoon-weight shape. I then use rubber bands to temporarily hold the lead in place while I float the decoy, mark the placement of the lead, and then attach it with copper brads.

The final touch is a copper name tag that I had made for my rig decoys. I attach this to the decoy with copper brads as well. The decoy is now finished.

MASTER TIP

Aging Copper and Lead

Because I live far from salt water, I have to make my own solutions in which to store metal hardware to give it an old look. Step 31 shows the lead and copper hardware before I aged it. In Step 32, you can see the rust that resulted from the salt water solution in which I soaked the hardware. Depending on the amount of rust and aging you want to achieve, this salt water process can take a week or more.

Antiquing Characteristics Reference Guide

Details. Details. Details. From head to tail and bill to cape, the carver needs to pay attention to the details that give a contemporary antique duck decoy an aged look. This involves employing techniques such as applying heat to the wood to produce cracking; using sandpaper to simulate wear and tear; using stones and chains to create dings and dents; and adding old hardware (or hardware made to look old) like weights, leather tabs, and fasteners for the appearance of authenticity. Here is a look at some of the effects you can achieve.

Crown

Neck

Weight

Anchor Ring

Tail

Bottom

Leather Tab

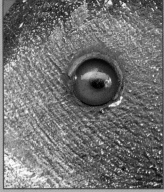

Eye

Bill Underside

Eye

Cape

Side

Weight (Removed)

Tail

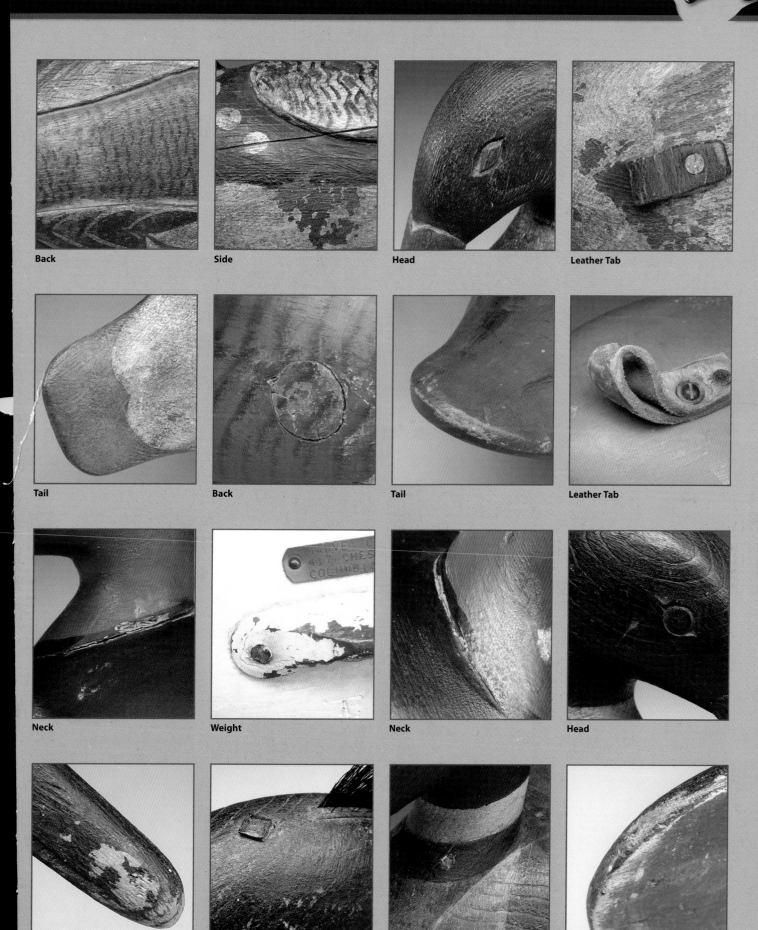

Back

Side

Head

Leather Tab

Tail

Back

Tail

Leather Tab

Neck

Weight

Neck

Head

Bill

Fastener (Top of Head)

Neck

Tail Underside

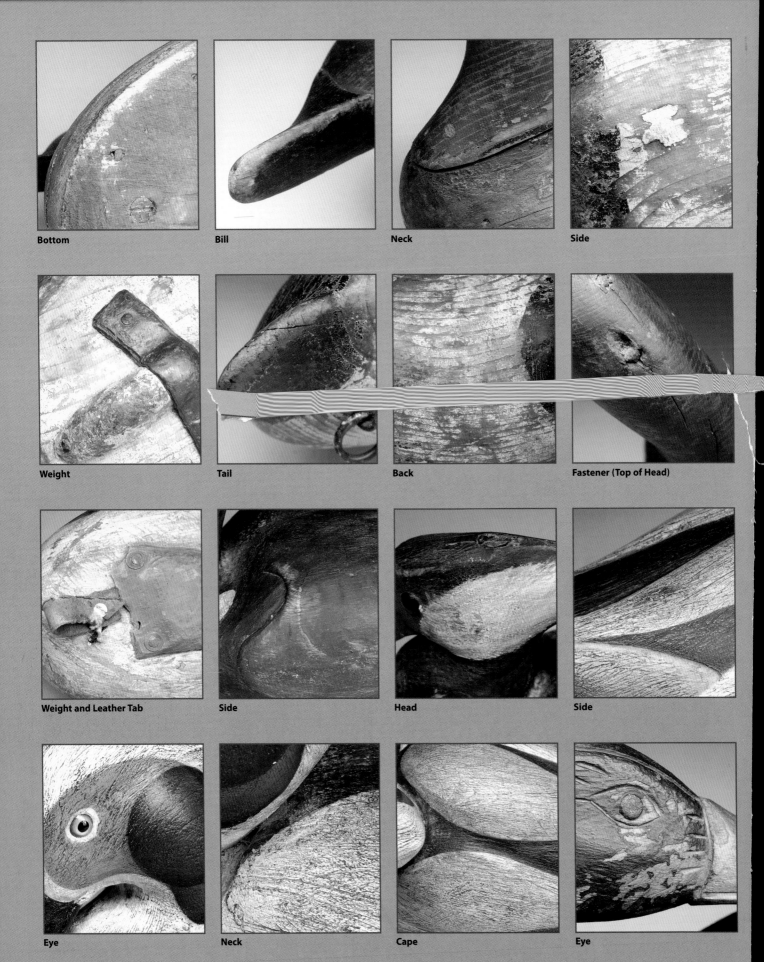

Bottom

Bill

Neck

Side

Weight

Tail

Back

Fastener (Top of Head)

Weight and Leather Tab

Side

Head

Side

Eye

Neck

Cape

Eye

Side

Wing

Tail Underside

Weight

Tail/Cape

Decoy Line (Neck)

Decoy Line (Bottom)

Eye

Neck

Side

Anchor Ring

Chain Weight

Side

Bottom

Side

Neck

References:

Bellrose, Frank C. *Ducks, Geese, and Swans of North America*, 1980, reprint, includes wildfowl management topics and species.

Terres, John K. *The Audubon Society Encyclopedia of North American Birds*, 1991, reprint, includes biological and ornithological reference.

Resources:

The Duck Blind
PO Box 706
Delton, MI 49046
1-800-852-7352
www.theduckblind.com
Vise, combs

JansenArt Traditions Paint
PO Box 290
Smoketown, PA 17576
(717) 361-2136
www.jansenarttraditions.com
Paints, painting supplies

Tupelo Timber
Steve Young
150 Oakwood Dr.
Brantford, ON N3T 5L7 Canada
(519) 751-1354
www.tupelotimber.ca
Decoy-sized wood, white cedar

Wood Carving Illustrated
1970 Broad St.
East Petersburg, PA 17520
1-800-457-9112
www.woodcarvingillustrated.com
How-to magazine for carving enthusiasts

Wildfowl Carving Magazine
1300 Market St., Suite 202
Lemoyne, PA 17043-1420
1-888-512-8008
www.wildfowl-carving.com
Magazine for wildfowl carvers and collectors

Jennings Decoy Co.
601 Franklin Ave., N.E.
St. Cloud, MN 56304
U.S. 1-800-331-5613
Canada (320) 253-2253
www.jenningsdecoycompany.com
Carving supplies, wildlife giftware